Extra Practice for
PRIMARY MATHEMATICS

4

TINOH CHAN

Marshall Cavendish
Education

PREFACE

Extra Practice *for* Primary Mathematics (U.S. Edition) is a series of six supplementary books that will prove invaluable to students in their understanding of mathematical concepts.

This series follows the topical arrangement in the Primary Mathematics U.S. Edition series. The exercises provide problems of a similar style and level of difficulty as the course material covered in the Primary Mathematics U.S. Edition series. The exercises are short and specific, so instructors may assign only those topics in which the student needs more practice. This, together with the simple language used, will allow students to review mathematics with minimal guidance.

The practice material aims to consolidate and reinforce the mathematical skills taught in the Primary Mathematics series.

© 2004 Marshall Cavendish International (Singapore) Private Limited
© 2014 Marshall Cavendish Education Pte Ltd

Published by Marshall Cavendish Education
Times Centre, 1 New Industrial Road, Singapore 536196
Customer Service Hotline: (65) 6213 9688
US Office Tel: (1-914) 332 8888 | Fax: (1-914) 332 8882
E-mail: cs@mceducation.com
Website: www.mceducation.com

First published 2004
Reprinted 2006, 2007, 2008, 2011, 2012, 2015, 2016, 2017, 2018, 2019, 2020 (twice), 2021

ISBN 978-981-01-9376-8

Printed in Singapore

CONTENTS

A. Write the numbers.

1. 16 thousands 8 tens   _____

2. 27 thousands 5 ones   _____

3. 80 thousands 4 tens 2 ones   _____

4. 95 thousands 6 hundreds   _____

B. Write the following in figures.

5. Seven thousand, three hundred five dollars   _____

6. Fifteen thousand, nine hundred twelve dollars   _____

7. Ninety thousand, thirteen dollars   _____

8. Eleven thousand, four hundred sixty dollars   _____

C. Write the following in words.

9. $30,180   _____

10. $19,011   _____

11. 80,818   _____

12. 25,370   _____

D. Complete the number patterns.

13. 6800, 7000, _____, _____, 7600.

14. 3056, 13,056, 23,056, _____, _____.

15. 5600, 10,600, 15,600, _____, _____.

16. 9762, 10,062, _____, 10,662, _____.

E. Fill in the blanks.

17. $85,009 = 80,000 + \boxed{} + 9$

18. $30,125 = \boxed{} + 5 + 100$

19. $20,000 + 60 + 6 + 2000 = \boxed{}$

20. $\boxed{} - 1000 = 19,218$

21. In 73,610, the digit 3 stands for $\boxed{}$.

22. In 68,245, the digit $\boxed{}$ is in the ten-thousands place. The value of the digit is $6 \times \boxed{}$.

23. In 49,051, the digit 0 is in the $\boxed{}$ place.

24. In 56,378, the hundreds digit is $\boxed{}$ and the thousands digit is $\boxed{}$.

2

F. Fill in the blanks.

25. ⬚ is 1000 less than 50,326.

26. There are ⬚ hundreds in 60,000.

27. ⬚ is 100 less than 72,000.

28. 566 is ⬚ when rounded off to the nearest ten.

29. A piano costs $3049.
Round off this amount to the nearest $100. ⬚ .

G. Arrange the numbers in increasing order.

30. 6538,   6385,   36,058,   30,568

_____

31. 40,105,   51,002,   39,278,   41,062

_____

H. Multiply and divide.

32. 5000 × 6 = _____

33. 12,000 × 8 = _____

34. 72,000 ÷ 4 = _____

35. 90,000 ÷ 6 = _____

3

Addition and Subtraction

A. Find the value of each of the following.

1. $\begin{array}{r} 3325 \\ + 698 \\ \hline \end{array}$

2. $\begin{array}{r} 6999 \\ + 777 \\ \hline \end{array}$

3. $\begin{array}{r} 7396 \\ + 1668 \\ \hline \end{array}$

4. $\begin{array}{r} 1348 \\ + 9878 \\ \hline \end{array}$

5. $\begin{array}{r} 9174 \\ + 3826 \\ \hline \end{array}$

6. $\begin{array}{r} 8297 \\ + 1998 \\ \hline \end{array}$

7. $\begin{array}{r} 4300 \\ - 1632 \\ \hline \end{array}$

8. $\begin{array}{r} 5000 \\ - 2899 \\ \hline \end{array}$

9. $\begin{array}{r} 8060 \\ - 5687 \\ \hline \end{array}$

10. $\begin{array}{r} 1004 \\ - 987 \\ \hline \end{array}$

11. $\begin{array}{r} 9011 \\ - 2999 \\ \hline \end{array}$

12. $\begin{array}{r} 7236 \\ - 6299 \\ \hline \end{array}$

B. Do these problems. Show all your work clearly.

13. Taylor has $173. She has $80 more than her brother. How much money do they have altogether?

14. There are 2058 students in a school. 1139 of them are girls. How many fewer boys than girls are there?

Factors and Multiples

A. Fill in the missing factors.

1. $42 = 6 \times \boxed{}$

2. $90 = 5 \times \boxed{}$

3. $100 = \boxed{} \times 4$

4. $9 \times \boxed{} = 72$

B. Find the factors of each number.

5. 18

6. 81

The factors of 18 are

_____ .

The factors of 81 are

_____ .

7. 56

8. 98

The factors of 56 are

_____ .

The factors of 98 are

_____ .

C. **Write a number in each** ☐ **to make the number sentence true.**

9. $12 \times 2 = 2 \times \boxed{} \times 3$

10. $12 \times 4 = \boxed{} \times 8 \times 2$

11. $6 \times 14 = 7 \times \boxed{}$

12. $35 \times 36 = 35 \times \boxed{} \times 4$

D. **Answer these questions. Show all your work clearly.**

13. Is 6 a common factor of 84 and 90?

14. What are the common factors of 12 and 18?

E. List the first four multiples of each number.

15. 3

The first four
multiples of 3 are

_____ .

16. 5

The first four
multiples of 5 are

_____ .

17. 7

The first four
multiples of 7 are

_____ .

18. 9

The first four
multiples of 9 are

_____ .

F. Find the first two common multiples of each set of numbers.

19. 6 and 9.

20. 3, 4 and 6

Multiplication and Division

A. Multiply.

1. $67 \times 8 =$

2. $89 \times 9 =$

3. $705 \times 6 =$

4. $596 \times 7 =$

5. $6879 \times 8 =$

6. $5068 \times 4 =$

B. Divide.

7. $112 \div 4 =$

8. $392 \div 7 =$

9. $840 \div 5 =$

10. $7248 \div 8 =$

11. $4428 \div 6 =$

12. $5067 \div 9 =$

C. Find the product of each pair of numbers.

13. 72 and 70

14. 568 and 90

15. 69 and 28

16. 800 and 50

17. 98 and 637

18. 509 and 46

D. Find the quotient and remainder when

19. 4002 is divided by 7.

20. 3915 is divided by 6.

Do these problems. Show all your work clearly.

1. Peter sold 25 boxes of oranges. Each box contained 78 oranges. If he sold 3 oranges for $1.00, how much money did he collect in all?

2. 8910 people visited a book fair. There were twice as many children as adults. How many children were there?

3. A guava weighs 402 g. It is 3 times as heavy as a pear. What is the total weight of the two fruits?

4. There are 36 boys and 43 girls in two classes. If each boy reads 8 books and each girl reads 12 books, how many books will they read altogether?

5.   There were 438 red chairs and 562 blue chairs in a hall. If there were 10 chairs in each row, how many rows were there?

6.   Pamela bought 7 kg of prawns at $18 per kg. After paying for them, she had $374 left. How much money did she have at first?

Equivalent Fractions

A. Find the missing numerators.

1. $\dfrac{1}{4} = \dfrac{\square}{8}$

2. $\dfrac{2}{5} = \dfrac{\square}{10}$

3. $\dfrac{5}{6} = \dfrac{\square}{18}$

4. $\dfrac{3}{8} = \dfrac{\square}{24}$

5. $\dfrac{1}{2} = \dfrac{\square}{20}$

6. $\dfrac{7}{9} = \dfrac{\square}{36}$

B. Find the missing denominators.

7. $\dfrac{1}{3} = \dfrac{3}{\square}$

8. $\dfrac{2}{3} = \dfrac{4}{\square}$

9. $\dfrac{3}{4} = \dfrac{9}{\square}$

10. $\dfrac{10}{25} = \dfrac{2}{\square}$

11. $\dfrac{24}{30} = \dfrac{4}{\square}$

12. $\dfrac{20}{28} = \dfrac{5}{\square}$

C. Complete these equivalent fractions.

13. $\dfrac{1}{2} = \dfrac{\square}{6} = \dfrac{6}{\square} = \dfrac{\square}{18}$

14. $\dfrac{3}{5} = \dfrac{9}{\square} = \dfrac{\square}{25} = \dfrac{24}{\square}$

D. **Express each of the following fractions in its simplest form.**

15. $\dfrac{6}{8}$ =

16. $\dfrac{5}{20}$ =

17. $\dfrac{18}{27}$ =

18. $\dfrac{10}{15}$ =

19. $\dfrac{16}{32}$ =

20. $\dfrac{40}{60}$ =

E. **Arrange the fractions in increasing order.**

21. $\dfrac{10}{20}$, $\dfrac{4}{5}$, $\dfrac{7}{10}$ _____

22. $\dfrac{5}{6}$, $\dfrac{2}{3}$, $\dfrac{9}{12}$ _____

23. $\dfrac{2}{3}$, $\dfrac{5}{6}$, $\dfrac{5}{9}$ _____

F. Do these problems. Show all your work clearly.

24. Cameron drank $\frac{5}{8}$ ℓ of water. Dani drank $\frac{3}{4}$ ℓ of water. Who drank more?

25. A pumpkin weighs $\frac{4}{5}$ kg. A melon weighs $\frac{9}{10}$ kg. A papaya weighs $\frac{13}{20}$ kg. Which is the heaviest? Which is the lightest?

Adding Fractions

A. Write the missing numbers.

1. $\dfrac{3}{4} + \dfrac{1}{8}$

    $= \boxed{} + \dfrac{1}{8}$

    $= \boxed{}$

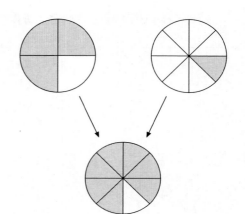

2. $\dfrac{1}{6} + \dfrac{1}{3}$

    $= \dfrac{1}{6} + \boxed{}$

    $= \boxed{}$

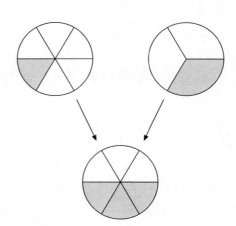

B. Add. Write the answers in the simplest form.

3. $\dfrac{1}{5} + \dfrac{1}{5} =$	4. $\dfrac{2}{7} + \dfrac{3}{7} =$	5. $\dfrac{7}{10} + \dfrac{1}{10} =$

6. $\dfrac{4}{12} + \dfrac{4}{12} =$	7. $\dfrac{1}{9} + \dfrac{5}{9} =$	8. $\dfrac{1}{2} + \dfrac{1}{2} =$

C.   Add. Write the answers in the simplest form.

9. $\dfrac{1}{5} + \dfrac{3}{10} =$	10. $\dfrac{1}{3} + \dfrac{2}{6} =$	11. $\dfrac{1}{10} + \dfrac{1}{2} =$
12. $\dfrac{5}{12} + \dfrac{1}{3} =$	13. $\dfrac{2}{4} + \dfrac{2}{8} =$	14. $\dfrac{3}{4} + \dfrac{2}{12} =$

D.   Add. Write the answers in the simplest form.

15. $\dfrac{1}{4} + \dfrac{1}{4} + \dfrac{1}{4} =$	16. $\dfrac{2}{6} + \dfrac{1}{6} + \dfrac{2}{6} =$
17. $\dfrac{2}{8} + \dfrac{3}{8} + \dfrac{1}{8} =$	18. $\dfrac{1}{3} + \dfrac{1}{3} + \dfrac{1}{3} =$
19. $\dfrac{5}{10} + \dfrac{3}{10} + \dfrac{2}{10} =$	20. $\dfrac{1}{12} + \dfrac{7}{12} + \dfrac{2}{12} =$

A. Subtract.

1.

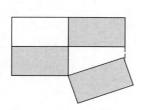

$$\frac{3}{4} - \frac{1}{4} =$$

2.

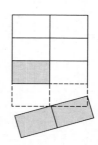

$$\frac{3}{8} - \frac{2}{8} =$$

B. Write the missing numbers.

3. $\frac{2}{3} - \frac{1}{6}$

$= \boxed{} - \frac{1}{6}$

$= \boxed{}$

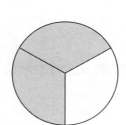

4. $\frac{7}{8} - \frac{3}{4}$

$= \frac{7}{8} - \boxed{}$

$= \boxed{}$

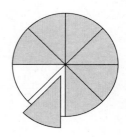

C. Subtract. Write the answers in the simplest form.

5. $\dfrac{3}{4} - \dfrac{1}{4} =$	6. $\dfrac{4}{5} - \dfrac{2}{5} =$	7. $1 - \dfrac{4}{7} =$
8. $\dfrac{7}{9} - \dfrac{4}{9} =$	9. $\dfrac{8}{10} - \dfrac{6}{10} =$	10. $\dfrac{11}{12} - \dfrac{9}{12} =$

D. Subtract. Write the answers in the simplest form.

11. $\dfrac{5}{6} - \dfrac{2}{3} =$	12. $\dfrac{3}{4} - \dfrac{2}{8} =$	13. $\dfrac{2}{3} - \dfrac{1}{9} =$
14. $\dfrac{4}{5} - \dfrac{3}{10} =$	15. $\dfrac{7}{12} - \dfrac{1}{3} =$	16. $1 - \dfrac{2}{10} =$

E. Subtract. Write the answers in the simplest form.

17. $\dfrac{3}{4} - \dfrac{1}{4} - \dfrac{1}{4} =$	18. $1 - \dfrac{3}{5} - \dfrac{1}{5} =$
19. $\dfrac{5}{7} - \dfrac{2}{7} - \dfrac{3}{7} =$	20. $\dfrac{8}{9} - \dfrac{4}{9} - \dfrac{1}{9} =$
21. $\dfrac{7}{10} - \dfrac{3}{10} - \dfrac{2}{10} =$	22. $1 - \dfrac{2}{12} - \dfrac{4}{12} =$

Word Problems on Fractions

Do these problems. Show all your work clearly.

1. Mary walked $\frac{4}{7}$ of the journey to the library.
   What fraction of the journey did she still have to walk?

2. A piece of cloth is $\frac{3}{8}$ ft long.

   Another piece of cloth is $\frac{1}{4}$ ft long.
   What is the total length of the 2 pieces of cloth?

3. Andrew and John shared an apple.
   Andrew ate $\frac{7}{12}$ of the apple and John ate $\frac{1}{3}$ of it.
   Who ate more? How much more?

4. Ann ate $\frac{1}{4}$ of a cake.

    Dylan ate $\frac{1}{4}$ of the cake more than Ann.
    What fraction of the cake did they eat altogether?

5. Susan had 1 kg of sugar.

    After she used $\frac{2}{5}$ kg, Siti gave her another $\frac{1}{10}$ kg of sugar.
    How much sugar did Susan have after that?

A. **Write a mixed number for each of the following.**

1. 2 wholes 1 half = _____

2. 3 wholes 2 thirds = _____

3. 2 wholes 3 quarters = _____

4. 7 wholes 5 eighths = _____

B. **Find the value of each of the following.**

5. $2 + \dfrac{7}{8}$ = _____   6. $\dfrac{3}{4} + 3$ = _____

7. $2 - \dfrac{2}{3}$ = _____   8. $5 - \dfrac{2}{5}$ = _____

C. **Write an improper fraction for each of the following.**

9. 10 fifths = _____   10. 9 quarters = _____

11. 18 sixths = _____   12. 11 thirds = _____

D. **Find the missing numerator in each of the following.**

13. $2 = \dfrac{\square}{6}$

14. $5 = \dfrac{\square}{2}$

15. $2\dfrac{3}{4} = 1\dfrac{\square}{4}$

16. $3\dfrac{2}{5} = 2\dfrac{\square}{5}$

17. $4\dfrac{2}{3} = 3\dfrac{\square}{3}$

18. $5\dfrac{5}{6} = 4\dfrac{\square}{6}$

E. **Change each improper fraction to a mixed number or a whole number.**

19. $\dfrac{9}{5} = $ _____

20. $\dfrac{18}{6} = $ _____

21. $\dfrac{15}{4} = $ _____

22. $\dfrac{19}{10} = $ _____

F. **Express each of the following as a whole number or a mixed number in its simplest form.**

23. $\dfrac{10}{6} = $ _____

24. $2\dfrac{10}{12} = $ _____

25. $5\dfrac{6}{4} = $ _____

26. $8\dfrac{5}{5} = $ _____

G. Add or subtract. Give each answer in its simplest form.

27. $1\frac{5}{8} + \frac{7}{8} =$ _____

28. $\frac{7}{10} + \frac{5}{10} =$ _____

29. $\frac{3}{4} + 6\frac{3}{4} =$ _____

30. $4\frac{5}{9} - \frac{2}{9} =$ _____

31. $2\frac{4}{7} - \frac{6}{7} =$ _____

32. $4 - 1\frac{3}{5} =$ _____

H. Express each mixed number as an improper fraction.

33. $1\frac{5}{6} =$ _____

34. $2\frac{7}{9} =$ _____

35. $3\frac{9}{10} =$ _____

36. $4\frac{7}{12} =$ _____

Continual Assessment 1

A. **Choose the correct answer and write its number in the parentheses provided. (40 points)**

1. How many hundreds are there in 6200?
   (1) 2   (2) 20
   (3) 62   (4) 200   (   )

2. The product of two numbers is 333. If one of the numbers is 9, the sum of the two numbers is _____ .
   (1) 342   (2) 324
   (3) 46   (4) 37   (   )

3. $8 \times 15 = 5 \times \boxed{}$. The missing factor in the box is
   _____ .
   (1) 3   (2) 24
   (3) 28   (4) 32   (   )

4. The quotient when 6120 is divided by 6 is _____ .
   (1) 102   (2) 120
   (3) 1020   (4) 1200   (   )

5. Subtract 3789 from 4002. The difference when rounded off to the nearest ten is _____ .
   (1) 200   (2) 210
   (3) 220   (4) 300   (   )

6. The sum of two numbers is 4305. If one of them is 1298, what is the other?
   (1) 3117   (2) 3097
   (3) 3007   (4) 2017   (   )

7. The product of 268 and 45 when rounded off to the nearest 100 is _____ .
   (1) 12,000
   (2) 12,060
   (3) 12,100
   (4) 12,200   (   )

8. The smallest 5-digit number that can be formed from 6, 1, 9, 8 and 3 is _____ .
   (1) 13,689
   (2) 13,986
   (3) 13,698
   (4) 31,689   (   )

9. Which of the following is a common multiple of 6 and 8?
   (1) 8
   (2) 16
   (3) 24
   (4) 32   (   )

10. There are 2318 students in a school. 1049 of them are boys. How many more girls are there?
    (1) 220
    (2) 320
    (3) 331
    (4) 1269   (   )

11. $2\frac{7}{8}$ expressed as an improper fraction is _____ .

    (1) $\frac{28}{7}$ (2) $\frac{22}{8}$ (3) $\frac{23}{8}$ (4) $\frac{27}{8}$ (   )

12. $3\frac{10}{6}$ expressed as a mixed number in its simplest form is _____ .

    (1) $4\frac{3}{5}$ (2) $4\frac{2}{3}$ (3) $4\frac{4}{6}$ (4) $5\frac{4}{5}$ (   )

13. $6 - \frac{1}{4} = \boxed{}$. The answer in the box is _____ .

    (1) $5\frac{3}{4}$ (2) $5\frac{1}{4}$ (3) $4\frac{3}{4}$ (4) $2\frac{1}{2}$ (   )

14. Arrange the fractions in increasing order.

$\frac{2}{5}$, $\frac{1}{2}$, $\frac{3}{10}$

(1) $\frac{1}{2}$, $\frac{2}{5}$, $\frac{3}{10}$ (2) $\frac{3}{10}$, $\frac{1}{2}$, $\frac{2}{5}$

(3) $\frac{3}{10}$, $\frac{2}{5}$, $\frac{1}{2}$ (4) $\frac{2}{5}$, $\frac{3}{10}$, $\frac{1}{2}$ (   )

15. $\frac{5}{8} = \frac{20}{\square}$. The missing denominator is _____.

(1) 4   (2) 16
(3) 32   (4) 40   (   )

16. The sum of $\frac{9}{10}$ and $\frac{6}{10}$ is _____.

(1) $1\frac{1}{5}$ (2) $1\frac{1}{3}$ (3) $1\frac{2}{5}$ (4) $1\frac{1}{2}$ (   )

17. If we subtract $\frac{4}{9}$ from $\frac{2}{3}$, the answer is _____.

(1) $\frac{2}{9}$ (2) $\frac{2}{3}$ (3) $\frac{4}{6}$ (4) $\frac{4}{9}$ (   )

18. A shopkeeper had $\frac{9}{10}$ kg of mushrooms. After selling some, he had $\frac{1}{2}$ kg of mushrooms left. How many kilograms of mushrooms had he sold?

(1) $\frac{1}{5}$ kg   (2) $\frac{2}{5}$ kg

(3) $\frac{3}{5}$ kg   (4) $\frac{3}{10}$ kg   (   )

19. A string 28 yd long is cut into 10 equal pieces. What is the length of each piece?

   (1) $2\frac{1}{5}$ yd   (2) $2\frac{2}{5}$ yd

   (3) $2\frac{3}{5}$ yd   (4) $2\frac{4}{5}$ yd   (   )

20. Kathy had 138 stamps. She kept 58 stamps for herself and gave the rest to a group of friends. Each friend received 5 stamps. How many friends were there in the group?

   (1) 12   (2) 14
   (3) 16   (4) 18   (   )

B. Do these problems and fill in the answers in the boxes provided. (40 points)

21. Forty thousand fifteen written in figures is _____ .

22. In 8532, 9132, ⬚, 10,332, 10,932, the missing number is _____ .

23. 37,463 − ⬚ = 30,000 + 7000 + 63. The missing number in the box is _____ .

24. _____ is 100 less than 90,000.

25. In 58,076, the value of the digit 8 is
    8 × _____ .

26. In 49,623, the digit 6 is in the _____ place.

27. Round off $78,951 to the nearest $100.

28. The factors of 20 are 1, 2, 4, [   ], [   ],
    and 20. The missing factors are _____
    and _____ .

29. The common factor of 15 and 10 is _____ .

30. The first common multiple of 9 and 12 is
    _____ .

31. $3\frac{5}{12}$ expressed as an improper fraction is
    _____ .

32. $\frac{21}{9}$ expressed as a mixed number in its simplest
    form is _____ .

30

33. Arrange the fractions in increasing order.

$$\frac{1}{2}, \quad \frac{3}{4}, \quad \frac{5}{8}$$

34. $2\frac{2}{5} = 1\frac{\square}{5}$. The missing numerator is _____.

35. The sum of $\frac{5}{9}$ and $\frac{7}{9}$ in its simplest form is

_____.

36. The difference between $\frac{11}{12}$ and $\frac{2}{3}$ is _____.

37. If we subtract $\frac{4}{5}$ from $4\frac{2}{5}$, the difference is

_____.

38. Siti's mother had $\frac{7}{8}$ lb of sugar. She used $\frac{1}{4}$ lb of

sugar for making pudding and $\frac{1}{2}$ lb for baking

a cake. How much sugar did she have left?

39 Mrs. Chen baked a cake. She gave $\frac{1}{4}$ of it to

her neighbor and ate $\frac{3}{8}$ of it. How much

cake did she have left?

40. The sum of two numbers is 50. If one number
is smaller than the other by 12, find the bigger
number.

C. Answer these questions. Show all your work clearly. (20 points)

41. Steve bought a refrigerator for $1268, a coffee maker for $218 and a television set which cost $486 less than the refrigerator. How much did he pay in all?

42. Mr. Smith bought a table and 6 chairs. He gave the cashier $1000 and received $30 change. If the chairs cost $58 each, what was the cost of the table?

43. A dictionary and a calculator cost $80. If the calculator cost $20 more than the dictionary, find the cost of the dictionary.

44. Fatimah saved $100 in 5 months. She saved $18 a month in the first three months. She saved $25 in the fourth month. How much did she save in the fifth month?

45. 200 coins are sorted and kept in 3 bags. The first bag has 20 more coins than the second bag. The second bag has twice as many coins as the third bag. How many coins are there in the third bag?

Multiplying Fractions

A. Multiply. Give each answer in its simplest form.

1. $\frac{1}{2} \times 9 =$	2. $\frac{1}{2} \times 16 =$
3. $\frac{1}{3} \times 12 =$	4. $\frac{2}{3} \times 9 =$
5. $\frac{4}{5} \times 10 =$	6. $\frac{7}{8} \times 12 =$
7. $\frac{5}{6} \times 4 =$	8. $\frac{3}{4} \times 20 =$

B. Multiply. Give each answer in its simplest form.

9. $4 \times \frac{2}{3}$ = W	10. $6 \times \frac{3}{4}$ = Y	11. $15 \times \frac{1}{2}$ = S
12. $8 \times \frac{3}{4}$ = E	13. $10 \times \frac{5}{6}$ = L	14. $12 \times \frac{1}{8}$ = A
15. $7 \times \frac{2}{3}$ = I	16. $9 \times \frac{3}{5}$ = T	17. $20 \times \frac{3}{10}$ = E

18. Write the letters which match the answers to find out what
     Dr. Lin says.

$$\overline{\quad}\ \ \overline{\quad}\ \ \overline{\quad} \qquad \overline{\quad}\ \ \overline{\quad}\ \ \overline{\quad}\ \ \overline{\quad}\ \ \overline{\quad}\ \ \overline{\quad}$$
$$6 \quad 1\frac{1}{2} \quad 5\frac{2}{5} \qquad\qquad 2\frac{2}{3} \quad 4\frac{2}{3} \quad 7\frac{1}{2} \quad 6 \quad 8\frac{1}{3} \quad 4\frac{1}{2}$$

A. Find the value of each of the following.

1. $\frac{1}{3}$ of 24 =	2. $\frac{1}{5}$ of 30 =
3. $\frac{1}{9}$ of 180 =	4. $\frac{1}{10}$ of 100 =
5. $\frac{3}{5}$ of 40 =	6. $\frac{5}{6}$ of 42 =
7. $\frac{8}{9}$ of 108 =	8. $\frac{7}{10}$ of 160 =

B. Find the value of each of the following.

9. $\frac{1}{2}$ of 15 =	10. $\frac{1}{3}$ of 10 =
11. $\frac{1}{5}$ of 28 =	12. $\frac{1}{4}$ of 30 =
13. $\frac{2}{3}$ of 25 =	14. $\frac{5}{6}$ of 14 =
15. $\frac{5}{8}$ of 20 =	16. $\frac{3}{10}$ of 15 =

A. Give each answer in its simplest form.

1. Express 40¢ as a fraction of $1.

2. Express 60 cm as a fraction of 1 m.

3. Express 45 minutes as a fraction of 1 hour.

4. What fraction of 1 m is 35 cm?

5. What fraction of 1 right angle is 60°?

6. What fraction of 1 day is 6 hours?

B. Do these problems. Show all your work clearly.

7. In a class of 42 students, 14 wear glasses. What fraction of the students wear glasses?

8. Jane has 60 stamps. 36 of them are Canadian stamps. What fraction of her stamps are Canadian stamps?

9. Mother bought a bag of 80 buttons. She used 16 of them. What fraction of the buttons were used?

10. A balsam plant is 25 cm tall. Express 25 cm as a fraction of 1 m.

Do these problems. Show all your work clearly.

1. A bottle of cooking oil weighs $\frac{3}{5}$ kg. A can of beans weighs $\frac{1}{4}$ kg. What is the total weight of 10 bottles of cooking oil and 12 cans of beans?

2. There are 36 peach trees in an orchard. $\frac{2}{9}$ of them are flowering. How many peach trees are **not** flowering?

3. 64 birds took part in a singing competition. $\frac{3}{4}$ of them were male. How many birds were female?

4. Paige saved $100. She spent $\frac{2}{5}$ of it to buy a watch. How much did the watch cost? How much money did she have left?

5. There are 30 people at a show. $\frac{3}{10}$ of them are children. The rest are adults. How many adults are there?

6. $\frac{3}{5}$ of the students in a class are girls. There are 24 girls in the class. How many students are there in the class? How many boys are there?

7. Madison spent $\frac{7}{10}$ of her money to buy a kettle. The kettle cost $56. How much money did she have at first? How much money did she have left?

8. There are 72 passengers on a bus. $\frac{5}{8}$ of them are adults. If there are 26 women, how many men are there?

9. A man bought 180 pineapples. He sold $\frac{5}{6}$ of them at $3 each and threw away the rest. How much money did he collect from the sale?

A. The table below shows a group of students who took part in school activities.
Use the table to answer the questions which follow.

Type of activities	Boys	Girls
Swimming	23	28
Volleyball	18	20
Choir	15	25
Drama Club	10	16

1. How many students took part in Swimming? _____

2. How many fewer students took part in Drama Club than in Volleyball? _____

3. How many more girls than boys took part in Volleyball and Choir? _____

4. If each student in the Choir pays $3 to buy a music book, how much do they pay in all? _____

B. The table below shows the data of workers in a factory.

5. Complete the table and answer the questions which follow:

	Number of men	**Number of women**	**Total Number**
Married workers	19		36
Single workers		36	
Total number =	32		

6. How many fewer male workers than female workers are there? _____

7. How many more single workers than married workers are there? _____

8. If 12 workers in the factory are above 40 years old, how many workers are below this age? _____

C. **The bar graph shows the number of tickets sold at a cinema in a week. Study the graph and answer the questions which follow.**

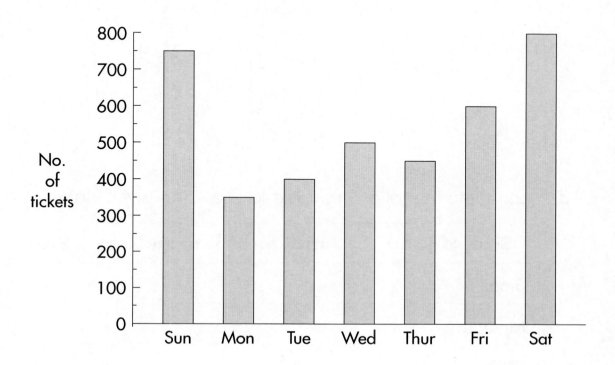

9. What is the total number of tickets sold on Saturday and Sunday? _____

10. How many tickets were sold from Monday to Friday? _____

11. How many more tickets were sold on Friday than on Monday? _____

12. On Saturday, if 265 tickets were sold at $8.00 each and the rest at $6.00 each, how much money did the cinema collect in all? _____

D. **The diagram shows the prices of hair gel sold in jars of different sizes. Use it to answer questions 13 to 16.**

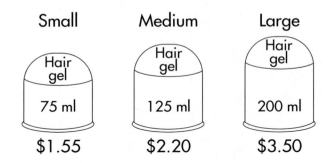

Small   Medium   Large

Hair gel   75 ml   Hair gel   125 ml   Hair gel   200 ml

$1.55 $2.20 $3.50

13. Complete the following table to show the given data.

Size of jar	Amount of hair gel	Price
Small		
Medium		
Large		

14. The shopkeeper sold 2 large jars and 3 small jars of hair gel. How much did he collect altogether?

46

15. Alicia bought 1 small jar and 2 medium-sized jars of hair gel. She gave the cashier $10. How much change did she receive?

16. How much cheaper is it to buy only a 200 ml jar of hair gel instead of a 75 ml jar and a 125 ml jar of hair gel?

A. **Mark the angles of each figure. Then complete the sentence below it.**

1.

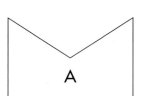

Figure A has _____ angles.

2.

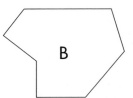

Figure B has _____ angles.

3.

Figure C has _____ angles.

4.

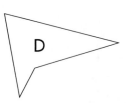

Figure D has _____ angles.

B. Mark all the right angles in each figure. Then complete the sentence below it.

5.

There are _____
right angles.

6.

There are _____
right angles.

7.

There are _____
right angles.

8.

There are _____
right angles

C. Use the picture to help you complete the table below.

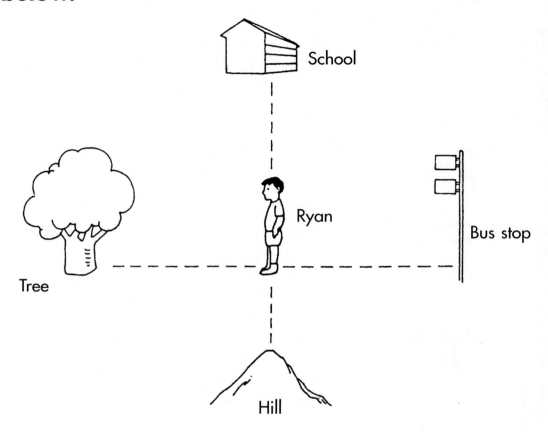

	Ryan is facing the	If he turns	He will face the
eg.	tree	1 right angle to the right	school
9.	tree	3 right angles to the left	
10.	bus stop	2 right angles	
11.	bus stop	3 right angles to the left	
12.	school	4 right angles	
13.	school	1 right angle to the right	
14.	hill	3 right angles to the left	
15.	hill	2 right angles	

A. **List all the marked angles in the table below.**

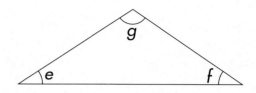

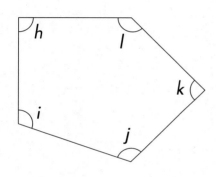

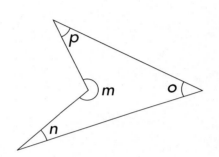

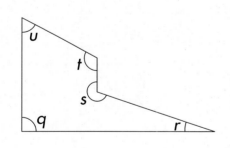

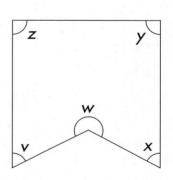

1.	Right angles	
2.	Smaller than a right angle	
3.	Greater than a right angle	

B. Measure the marked angles.

4.

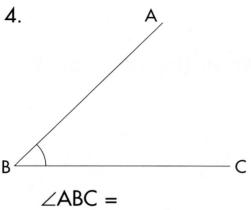

∠ABC =

5.

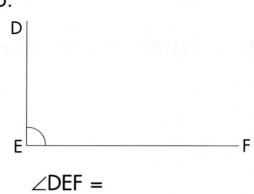

∠DEF =

6.

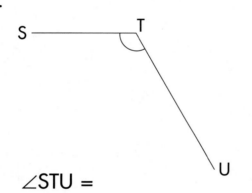

∠STU =

7.

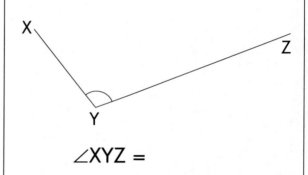

∠XYZ =

8.

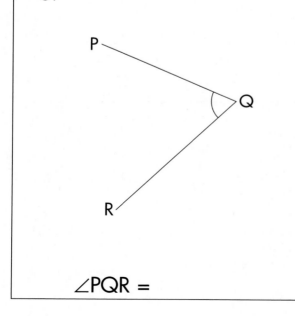

∠PQR =

9.

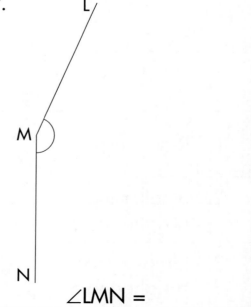

∠LMN =

C. Use the marked end point of each line to make the required angle. Mark the angle.

10. $\angle a = 75°$	11. $\angle b = 38°$
12. $\angle c = 110°$	13. $\angle d = 165°$
14. $\angle e = 123°$	15. $\angle f = 136°$

A. Find the unknown marked angles in each of the following rectangles.

1.

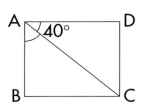

∠BAC =

2.

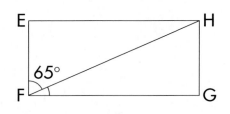

∠GFH =

3.

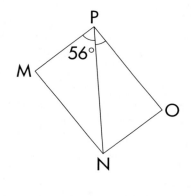

∠NPO =

4.

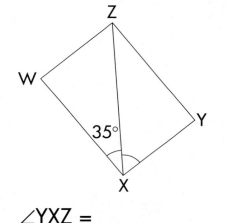

∠YXZ =

B. Find the unknown marked angles in each of the following figures.

5.

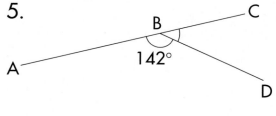

∠CBD =

6.

∠STV =

A. Fill in the blanks.

1. A complete turn is _____ right angles.
   It is _____ degrees.

2. $\frac{1}{2}$ of a complete turn is _____ right angles.
   It is _____ degrees.

3. $\frac{1}{4}$ of a complete turn is _____ right angle.
   It is _____ degrees.

4. $\frac{3}{4}$ of a complete turn is _____ right angles.
   It is _____ degrees.

B. Measure the marked angles.

5.   6.

∠a = _____   ∠b = _____

7.

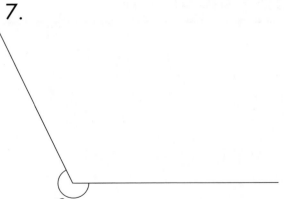

∠c = _____

8.

∠f = _____

C. The following figures are not drawn to scale. Find the unknown marked angles.

9.

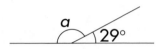

∠a = _____

10.

∠b = _____

11.

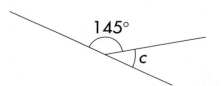

∠c = _____

12.

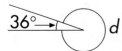

∠d = _____

13.

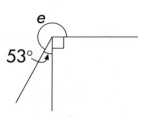

∠e = _____

14.

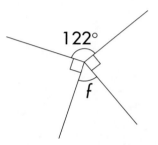

∠f = _____

56

Perpendicular Lines

A. Name each pair of perpendicular lines.

1.

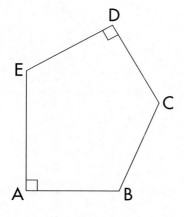

2.

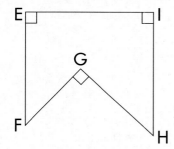

3.

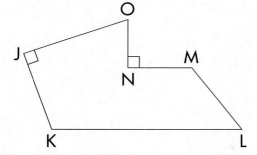

4.

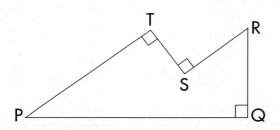

B. Draw a line perpendicular to each of the given lines through the point P.

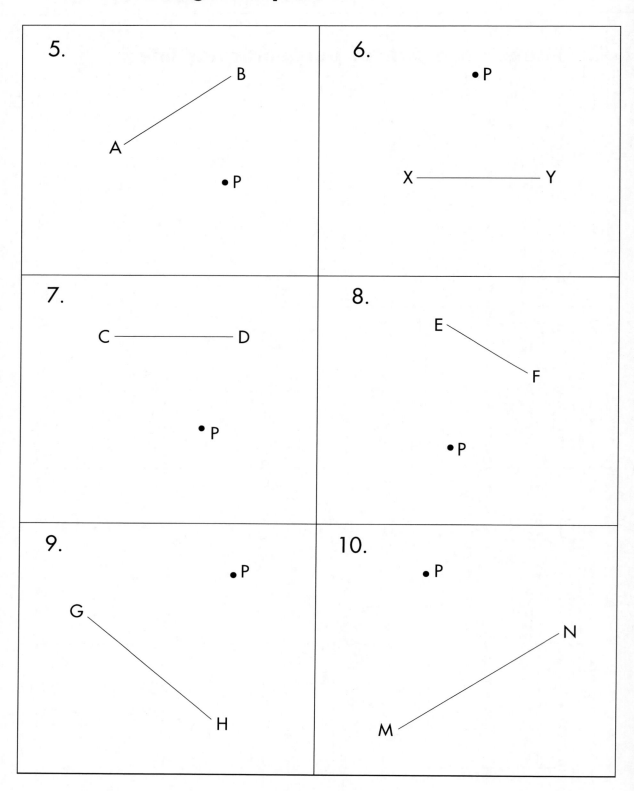

5.

B

A

• P

6.

• P

X ——————— Y

7.

C ——————— D

• P

8.

E

F

• P

9.

• P

G

H

10.

• P

N

M

A. Name all the pairs of parallel lines.

1.

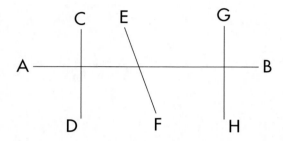

2.

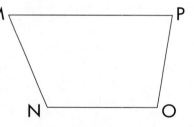

3.

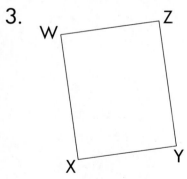

4.

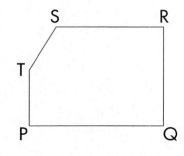

B. Use a set-square and a ruler to draw a line parallel to each of the given lines through the point P.

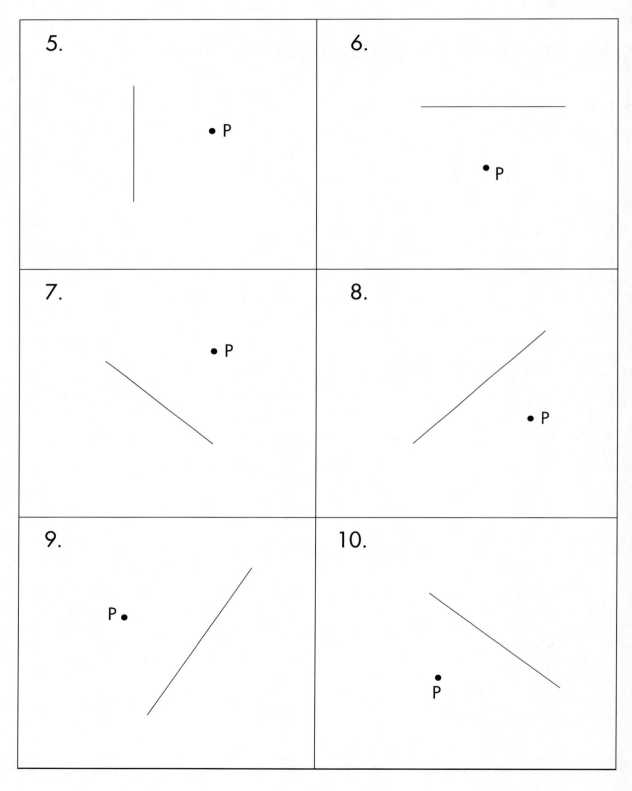

C. Fill in the blanks.

11. The figure is made up of a square and a rectangle.

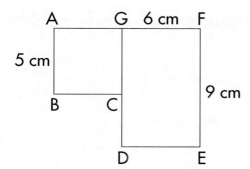

AB = 5 cm

EF = 9 cm

FG = 6 cm

CD = _____

AF = _____

12. The figure is made up of a rectangle and a square.

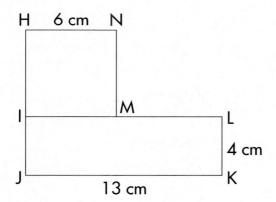

JK = 13 cm

KL = 4 cm

HN = 6 cm

ML = _____

HJ = _____

13. The figure is made up of a square and two rectangles.

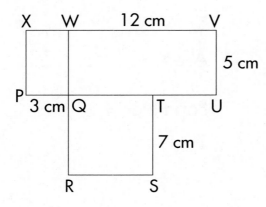

PQ = 3 cm

ST = 7 cm

UV = 5 cm

VW = 12 cm

TU = _____

PU = _____

WR = _____

61

A. Find the area and perimeter of each rectangle or square.

1.

3 cm

6 cm

Area = _____

Perimeter = _____

2.

4 cm

5 cm

Area = _____

Perimeter = _____

3.

6 m

6 m

Area = _____

Perimeter = _____

B. Do these problems. Show all your work clearly.

4. Kyle uses 18 old stamps to make a picture. If each stamp measures 3 cm by 2 cm, find the area of the picture.

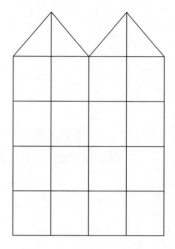

5. Cameron wants to carpet his living room floor which measures 8 yd by 4 yd. If the carpet costs $15 per square yard, how much must Cameron pay to buy the carpet he needs?

6. A rectangular garden measures 28 m by 16 m. What is the cost of putting up a fence around it if 1 m of fencing costs $9?

7. The perimeter of a square is 32 cm. Find its area.

8. The area of a rectangle is 24 in.^{2}. If the width of the rectangle is 4 in., find its perimeter.

9. The square and the rectangle have the same perimeter.

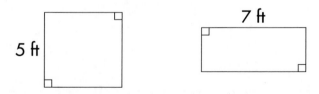

(a) Find the width of the rectangle.

(b) Which figure has a bigger area?

10. The area of a rectangle is 30 m². If the length of the rectangle is 6 m, find its width and perimeter.

11. Find the unknown side and the area of each of the following rectangles.

(a)

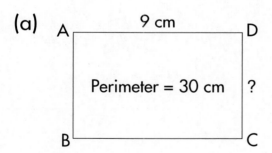

(b)

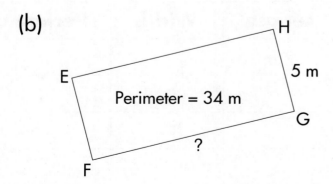

12. Find the unknown side and the perimeter of each of the following rectangles.

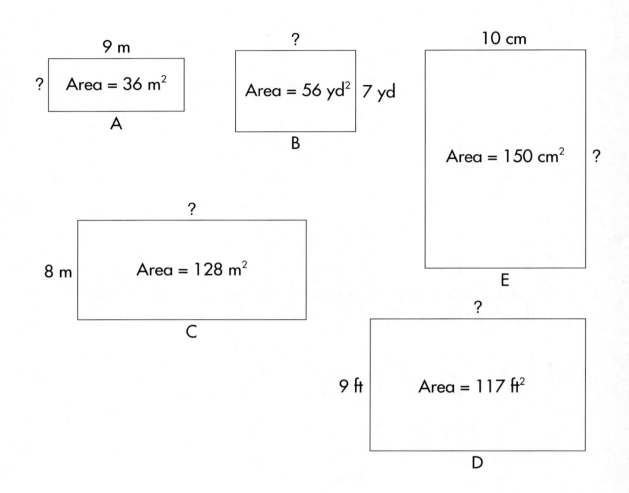

Figure	Area	Length	Width	Perimeter
A	36 m²	9 m		
B	56 yd²		7 yd	
C	128 m²		8 m	
D	117 ft²		9 ft	
E	150 cm²		10 cm	

A. **Find the perimeter of each of the following figures. (All the angles are right angles.)**

1.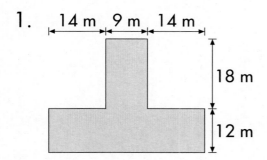

2.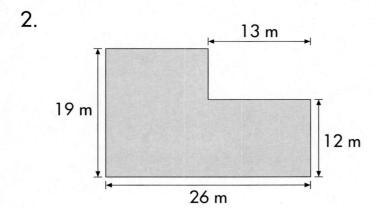

3.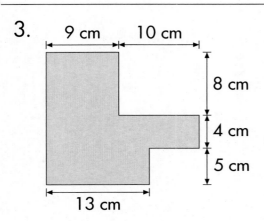

B. Find the area of each of the following figures.

4.

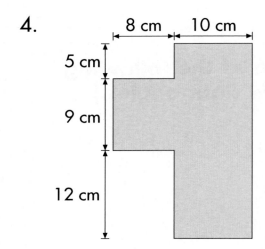

5.

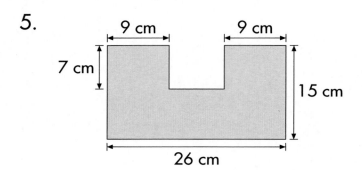

6.

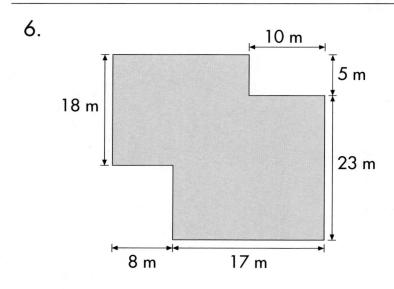

C. Find the area of the shaded part of each rectangle.

7.

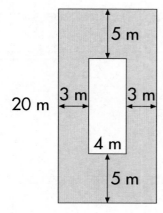

8.

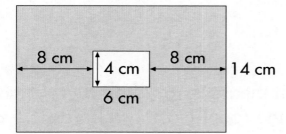

9.

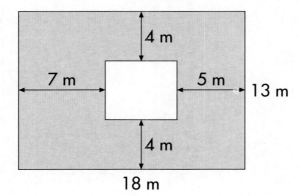

D. Do these problems. Show all your work clearly.

10. A rectangular garden measures 28 ft by 15 ft. A concrete path 1 ft wide is paved around it. What is the area of the path?

28 ft

15 ft

11. A rectangular living room measures 6 yd by 5 yd. A carpet is placed on the floor of the room leaving a border 1 yd wide all around it. Find the area of the border.

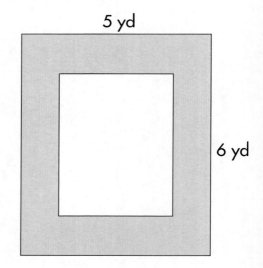

5 yd

6 yd

A. **Choose the correct answer and write its number in the parentheses provided. (40 points)**

1. 8899 is the same as _____ .
   (1) 88 + 99   (2) 889 + 9
   (3) 8099 + 800   (4) 8809 + 900   (   )

2. Which one of the following is the same as fifty hundreds?
   (1) 500   (2) 1500
   (3) 5000   (4) 50,000   (   )

3. [   ] ÷ 7 = 96 R 3. What is the missing number?
   (1) 678   (2) 675
   (3) 657   (4) 567   (   )

4. The largest number less than 60,000 that can be formed with the digits 9, 3, 6, 5 and 8 is _____ .
   (1) 58,936   (2) 56,839
   (3) 59,863   (4) 59,638   (   )

5. If $5 \times$ [   ] $\times 7 = 280$, the missing factor is _____ .
   (1) 6   (2) 8
   (3) 10   (4) 12   (   )

6. 9 is a common factor of 81 and _____ .
   (1) 146   (2) 130
   (3) 128   (4) 117   (   )

7. Which of the following figures has $\frac{3}{5}$ of it shaded?

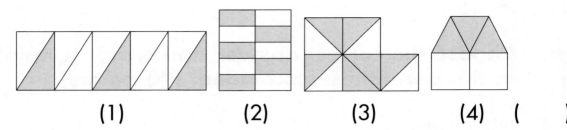

(1)   (2)   (3)   (4)   (   )

8. Which of the following is a common multiple of 3, 6 and 9?
   (1) 24   (2) 36
   (3) 45   (4) 60   (   )

9. The number of residents in a town was 38,000 when rounded off to the nearest hundred. Which one of the following could be the exact number of residents there?
   (1) 38,096   (2) 38,103
   (3) 37,895   (4) 37,952   (   )

10. $\frac{1}{4} + \frac{1}{12} + \boxed{} = 1$. The missing number is _____ .

    (1) $\frac{1}{2}$ (2) $\frac{1}{3}$ (3) $\frac{2}{3}$ (4) $\frac{5}{6}$ (   )

11. The sum of $\frac{2}{3}$ and $\frac{7}{12}$ is _____ .

    (1) $\frac{9}{15}$ (2) $\frac{3}{5}$ (3) $1\frac{1}{4}$ (4) $1\frac{3}{4}$ (   )

12. Which one of the following fractions is the smallest in value?

    (1) $\frac{1}{2}$ (2) $\frac{3}{8}$ (3) $\frac{3}{4}$ (4) $\frac{7}{12}$ (   )

13. A shopkeeper had 30 umbrellas. $\frac{3}{5}$ of them were red. If he

sold $\frac{2}{3}$ of the red umbrellas, how many red umbrellas did

he sell?
(1) 6   (2) 12   (3) 16   (4) 18   (   )

14. ABCD and CDEF are two similar squares.
Which line is parallel to CE?
(1) DF   (2) AC
(3) BD   (4) CD   (   )

15. Which of the following figures does not have any sets of
perpendicular lines?

(1) 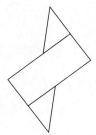   (2)

(3)    (4)

                                                  (   )

16. The perimeter of a rectangle is 38 cm. Its length is 12 cm.
Find its area.
(1) 84 cm²   (2) 96 cm²
(3) 316 cm²   (4) 456 cm²   (   )

17. Find the area of the shaded part.

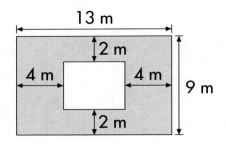

(1) 92 m²
(2) 85 m²
(3) 36 m²
(4) 25 m²
( )

18. Find the perimeter of the figure.

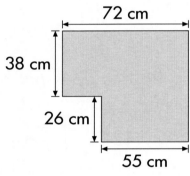

(1) 208 cm
(2) 255 cm
(3) 266 cm
(4) 272 cm
( )

19. Jane spent $\frac{3}{8}$ of her money on a pair of shoes. If the shoes cost $18, how much money did she have at first?
(1) $36   (2) $42   (3) $48   (4) $54   ( )

20. Dorothy bought $\frac{4}{5}$ kg of prawns. 1 kg of prawns cost $20. If she gave the cashier $100, how much change did she receive?
(1) $65   (2) $74   (3) $84   (4) $85   ( )

B. Do the problems and write the answers in the boxes provided. (40 points)

21. 5993 is _____ more than the product of 283 and 21.

22. Divide the difference between 1768 and 8150 by 6. The remainder is _____ .

23. 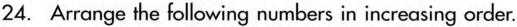 What fraction of the figure is shaded? Give your answer in its simplest form.

24. Arrange the following numbers in increasing order.

$$2, \quad \frac{5}{6}, \quad \frac{12}{8}, \quad \frac{7}{12}$$

25. Which one of the following is a common factor of 18 and 63?

$$63, \quad 36, \quad 9, \quad 6$$

26. Jordan had his car painted and its four tires replaced. He paid $1216 altogether. If the painting cost $900, how much did each tire cost?

27. Peter ate $\frac{1}{12}$ of a cake. His father ate $\frac{1}{4}$ more than him. What fraction of the cake did they eat altogether?

28. What fraction of 1 right angle is 15°? Give your answer in its simplest form.

29. Ryan saved $84 in 6 weeks. If he saved an equal amount each week, how much would he save in 26 weeks?

30. Twice as many movie tickets were sold on Saturday as on Friday. 120 fewer tickets were sold on Sunday than on Saturday. If 650 tickets were sold on Sunday, how many tickets were sold on Friday?

31. After spending $\frac{3}{5}$ of his savings, Connor had $24 left. How much savings did he have at first?

32. What number must be subtracted from $\frac{5}{6}$ to give $\frac{1}{12}$?

33. Logan painted $\frac{5}{12}$ of a wall. His wife painted $\frac{1}{4}$ of it. What fraction of the wall was not painted? Give your answer in its simplest form.

34. 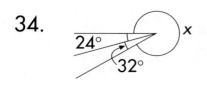 The figure is not drawn to scale. The unknown angle x is _____ degrees.

76

35. 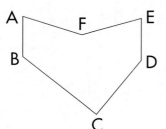 Name a pair of perpendicular lines.

36. 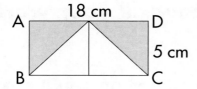 ABCD is a rectangle. The area of the shaded part is _____ .

37. A boy ran 8 times round a rectangular field measuring 52 m by 30 m. What was the distance he ran?

38. 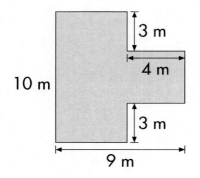 Find the area of the figure. (All the angles are right angles.)

The bar graph shows how the monthly income of a family is used. Use the graph to answer questions 39 and 40.

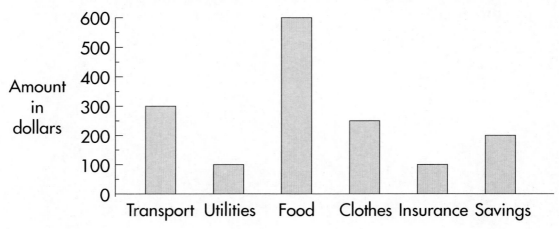

39. What is the total monthly expenditure of the family?

40. What is the total monthly income of the family?

C. Answer these questions. Show all your work clearly. (20 points)

41. Lina saved $110 in 5 months. She saved an equal amount in the first and second month. If she saved $18 each month in the last three months, how much did she save in the first month?

42. There are 19 girls and 23 boys in a class. If $\frac{2}{7}$ of the students failed their science test, how many of them passed the test?

43. Alexis had 1 lb of sugar. She used $\frac{3}{5}$ lb of it to make a cake and $\frac{1}{10}$ lb of it to make coffee. How much sugar had she left?

44. A man had 150 pumpkins. After throwing away 12 rotten pumpkins, he sold 48 of them at $4 each. He sold the rest at $3 each. How much money did he receive from the sale of the pumpkins?

45. Find the perimeter and area of the figure.
    (All the angles are right angles.)

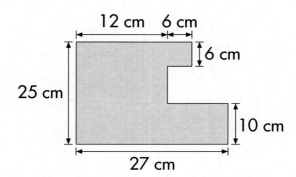

Decimals — Tenths

A. Write each fraction as a decimal.

1. $\dfrac{3}{10} =$

2. $\dfrac{8}{10} =$

3. $3\dfrac{5}{10} =$

4. $1\dfrac{6}{10} =$

5. $2\dfrac{7}{10} =$

6. $4\dfrac{9}{10} =$

B. Write each decimal as a fraction in its simplest form.

7. $0.6 =$

8. $0.5 =$

9. $0.2 =$

10. $1.8 =$

11. $3.4 =$

12. $5.3 =$

C.   Write the numbers in decimals

13.   6 ones 5 tenths =

14.   3 ones 9 tenths =

15.   5 tens 2 ones 6 tenths =

16.   8 tens 8 tenths =

D.   Fill in the missing decimal or whole number in each box.

17. $36.5 = 30 + 6 +$ ☐

18. $50.2 = 50 +$ ☐

19. $78.4 = 70 + 8 +$ ☐

20. $29.3 =$ ☐ tens + ☐ ones + ☐ tenths

A. Write each fraction as a decimal.

1. $\dfrac{5}{100} =$

2. $\dfrac{8}{100} =$

3. $\dfrac{39}{100} =$

4. $\dfrac{63}{100} =$

5. $3\dfrac{1}{100} =$

6. $7\dfrac{6}{100} =$

7. $10\dfrac{99}{100} =$

8. $9\dfrac{56}{100} =$

B. Fill in the blanks.

9. In 28.09, the digit 9 is in the _____ place.
    Its value is _____ .

10. In 80.65, the digit 6 is in the _____ place.
    Its value is _____ .

C. Write the value of each of the following as a decimal.

11. $30 + \dfrac{2}{10} =$

12. $10 + 6 + \dfrac{9}{10} =$

13. $29 + \dfrac{3}{100} =$

14. $62 + \dfrac{5}{10} + \dfrac{1}{100} =$

D. Fill in the missing decimals.

15. $8.88 = 8 + 0.8 +$ ⬚

16. $12.07 = 10 + 2 +$ ⬚

17. $34.45 = 30 + 4 +$ ⬚ $+ 0.05$

18. $59.11 = 50 + 9 +$ ⬚ $+$ ⬚

E. Fill in the blanks.

19. $0.9 =$ _____ tenths

20. $1.3 =$ _____ tenths

21. $2.5 =$ _____ tenths

22. $0.05 =$ _____ hundredths

23. $0.36 =$ _____ hundredths

24. $0.7 =$ _____ hundredths

25. $1 =$ _____ hundredths

26. $1.8 =$ _____ hundredths

F. Complete the following number patterns.

27. $0.7, \quad 0.8,$ ⬚ $,$ ⬚ $, \quad 1.1, \quad 1.2$

28. $0.5, \quad 1,$ ⬚ $,$ ⬚ $, \quad 2.5, \quad 3$

29. $0.25, \quad 0.2,$ ⬚ $,$ ⬚ $, \quad 0.05$

30. $4, \quad 3.8,$ ⬚ $,$ ⬚ $, \quad 3.2, \quad 3$

31. $2, \quad 1.75, \quad 1.5,$ ⬚ $,$ ⬚ $, \quad 0.75$

83

G. Write each decimal as a fraction in its simplest form.

32. $0.8 =$

33. $7.4 =$

34. $0.25 =$

35. $3.75 =$

36. $0.06 =$

37. $4.02 =$

38. $0.35 =$

39. $8.45 =$

H. Change the denominator to 10 or 100. Then write the fraction as a decimal.

40. $\dfrac{1}{5} =$

41. $5\dfrac{1}{2} =$

42. $10\dfrac{2}{5} =$

43. $\dfrac{1}{4} =$

44. $\dfrac{3}{4} =$

45. $2\dfrac{3}{4} =$

46. $\dfrac{19}{20} =$

47. $4\dfrac{12}{25} =$

Decimals — Thousandths

A. Write each fraction as a decimal.

1. $\dfrac{7}{1000} =$

2. $\dfrac{9}{1000} =$

3. $\dfrac{23}{1000} =$

4. $\dfrac{56}{1000} =$

5. $\dfrac{135}{1000} =$

6. $\dfrac{792}{1000} =$

7. $9\dfrac{5}{1000} =$

8. $30\dfrac{18}{1000} =$

B. Fill in the blanks.

9. In 7.328, the digit 8 is in the _____ place.
   Its value is _____ .

10. In 59.043, the digit 3 is in the _____ place.
    Its value is _____ .

C. Fill in the missing decimals.

11. $6.512 = 6 + 0.5 + 0.01 +$ ☐

12. $23.086 = 23 + 0.08 +$ ☐

13. $10.227 = 10 + 0.2 + 0.02 +$ ☐

D. Fill in the blanks.

14. 0.007 = _____ thousandths

15. 0.039 = _____ thousandths

16. 1 = _____ thousandths

E. Write the value of each of the following as a decimal.

17. $12 + \dfrac{1}{1000} =$ _____

18. $8 + \dfrac{25}{1000} =$ _____

19. $25 + \dfrac{4}{10} + \dfrac{3}{1000} =$ _____

20. $7 + \dfrac{6}{100} + \dfrac{8}{1000} =$ _____

21. 2 thousandths = _____

22. 3 hundredths 8 thousandths = _____

23. 7 tenths 5 thousandths = _____

24. 6 ones 6 thousandths = _____

25. 9 tens 9 thousandths = _____

Comparing Decimals

A. Circle the smallest number in each set.

1. 2, 0.95, 1.8, 1.56

2. 1.37, 3.07, 7.3, 0.736

3. 6.999, 8.1, 9, 7.023

4. 0.9, 1.02, 0.86, 2.012

B. Circle the greatest number in the set.

5. 4.85, 4.90, 5, 4.998

6. 2.31, 3.60, 1.98, 4.01

7. 2.2, 1.93, 1.96, 0.995

8. 4.59, 6.1, 5.95, 4.8

C. Fill in the blanks.

9. 0.1 more than 29.9 is _____ .

10. _____ is 0.01 less than 59.69.

11. _____ is 0.1 more than 83.9.

12. 0.01 more than 62.29 is _____ .

13. 0.1 more than 76.89 is _____ .

14. _____ is 0.1 less than 28.93.

15. _____ is 0.01 more than 19.99.

16. _____ is 0.01 less than 30.1.

17. 0.1 less than 1 is _____ .

18. 0.01 more than 5.99 is _____ .

A. Fill in the blanks.

1. 5.6 is _____ when rounded off to the nearest whole number.

2. 12.3 is _____ when rounded off to the nearest whole number.

3. 29.43 is _____ when rounded off to the nearest whole number.

4. 60.51 is _____ when rounded off to the nearest whole number.

B. Round off each of the following to the nearest whole number.

5. 58.92 _____

6. 34.36 _____

7. 7.8 _____

8. 49.7 _____

9. 399.6 _____

10. 205.05 _____

11. $15.25 _____

12. $65.73 _____

C. Round off each of the following to the nearest kilogram.

13. 36.54 kg _____

14. 59.4 kg _____

D. Round off each of the following to the nearest yard.

15. 22.15 yd _____   16. 91.52 yd _____

E. Round off each of the following to the nearest liter.

17. 4.63 ℓ _____   18. 17.45 ℓ _____

F. Round off each of the following to the nearest kilometer.

19. 64.48 km _____   20. 529.7 km _____

G. Round off each of the following to 1 decimal place.

21. 69.05 _____   22. 86.53 _____

23. 35.68 _____   24. 164.56 _____

25. 561.95 _____   26. 216.24 _____

H. Choose the best answer and write it in the box.

27. Diana weighs about 35 kg. Which one of the following could be her actual weight?

34.45 kg,   35.60 kg,   34.35 kg,   35.38 kg   [   ]

Addition of Decimals

Find each sum.

1. 0.6 + 0.4 =	2. 0.7 + 0.8 =
3. 3.2 + 0.8 =	4. 5.4 + 0.9 =
5. 5.7 + 3 =	6. 7.6 + 2.9 =
7. 5.2 + 30.8 =	8. 2.6 + 29 =
9. 40.2 + 8.8 =	10. 356.4 + 9.7 =
11. 275.9 + 10.3 =	12. 240 + 61.4 =

13. 4.85 + 3.65 =	14. 3.46 + 0.8 =
15. 0.05 + 5.95 =	16. 23.16 + 0.08 =
17. 0.56 + 4.69 =	18. 1.8 + 0.74 =
19. 9.56 + 14.64 =	20. 51.8 + 7.34 =
21. 5.36 + 85.9 =	22. 3.4 + 43.58 =
23. 91.65 + 19 =	24. 1.06 + 369 =

Find the differences.

1. 1.5 – 0.6 =	2. 3.1 – 1.3 =
3. 9.4 – 8.6 =	4. 7 – 3.4 =
5. 5 – 0.5 =	6. 8 – 0.1 =
7. 1 – 0.5 =	8. 28 – 0.8 =
9. 70 – 0.1 =	10. 5.2 – 0.4 =
11. 7.03 – 6.8 =	12. 100 – 39.7 =

13. 2.38 − 0.09 =	14. 1.4 − 0.04 =
15. 0.1 − 0.08 =	16. 8.7 − 0.09 =
17. 3 − 0.01 =	18. 12 − 0.02 =
19. 0.6 − 0.39 =	20. 9 − 0.25 =
21. 5 − 4.91 =	22. 10 − 5.32 =
23. 10.05 − 6.98 =	24. 25 − 7.06 =

Do these problems. Show all your work clearly.

1. Emma bought a storybook for $5.65 and a file for $4.80. She gave the cashier $20. How much change did she receive?

2. Tina is 1.53 m tall. She is 0.19 m shorter than her father. If her mother is 1.67 m tall, how much taller is her father than her mother?

3. Tyrone weighs 30.3 kg. He is 3.45 kg heavier than his sister. What is their total weight?

4. Caden bought a shirt and a belt. The shirt cost $14.75. The belt cost $6 more than the shirt. How much did he spend altogether?

Town A   Town B   Town C

5. The distance from Town A to Town B is 40.3 km. The distance from Town B to Town C is 3.95 km shorter than the distance from Town A to Town B. Find the distance from Town A to Town C.

6. String A is 0.8 m longer than String B. String B is 0.75 m shorter than String C. If String C is 4 m, find the total length of the 3 strings.

A. **Choose the correct answer and write its number in the parentheses provided. (40 points)**

1. 0.75 expressed as a fraction in its simplest form is
   _____ .

   (1) $\frac{2}{3}$ (2) $\frac{1}{4}$ (3) $\frac{3}{4}$ (4) $\frac{3}{5}$ (   )

2. $\boxed{} \div 5 = 750 + 880$. The missing number in the box
   is _____ .
   (1) 326   (2) 1625   (3) 1630   (4) 8150   (   )

3. How many right angles are equal to $\frac{3}{4}$ of a complete turn?
   (1) 1   (2) 2   (3) 3   (4) 4   (   )

4.
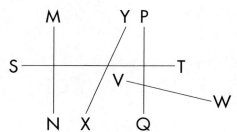

   In the figure, which line is parallel to MN?
   (1) ST   (2) XY   (3) PQ   (4) VW   (   )

5. 61.98 is $\boxed{}$ less than 62. The missing number in the
   box is _____ .
   (1) 0.02   (2) 0.12   (3) 1.98   (4) 0.2   (   )

6. 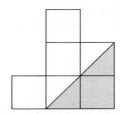 What fraction of the figure is shaded?

   (1) $\frac{1}{3}$　　(2) $\frac{2}{5}$

   (3) $\frac{4}{6}$　　(4) $\frac{4}{9}$　　(　)

7. How many hundredths are there in 5.69?
   (1) 5　　(2) 56　　(3) 69　　(4) 569　　(　)

8. $\frac{7}{8} \times 4 = 3 +$ ☐ . The missing decimal is _____ .
   (1) 0.2　　(2) 0.3　　(3) 0.5　　(4) 0.6　　(　)

9. What number must be added to the product of 19 and 48 to give the answer 1000?
   (1) 76　　(2) 88　　(3) 933　　(4) 1912　　(　)

10. Jake has 143 baseball cards. Sara has 255 baseball cards. How many baseball cards must Sara give Jake so that they will have an equal number of baseball cards?
    (1) 28　　(2) 34　　(3) 56　　(4) 68　　(　)

11. Which one of the following is the smallest?
    (1) 8　　(2) 8.02　　(3) 7.89　　(4) 9.01　　(　)

12. Which one of the following is equal to $\frac{5}{3}$?

    (1) $1\frac{6}{12}$　　(2) $1\frac{8}{12}$　　(3) $1\frac{9}{12}$　　(4) $1\frac{10}{12}$　　(　)

13. How many **one fifths** are there in $3\frac{3}{5}$?
    (1) 3　　(2) 8　　(3) 11　　(4) 18　　(　)

14. Write 76 tenths as a decimal.
    (1) 760.0   (2) 76.0   (3) 7.6   (4) 0.76   (   )

15. 209.96 when rounded off to 1 decimal place is _____ .
    (1) 209   (2) 209.9 (3) 210.0 (4) 208.0 (   )

16. Which one of the following is equal to $\frac{3}{4}$?

    (1) $\frac{9}{15}$ (2) $\frac{16}{24}$

    (3) $\frac{12}{16}$ (4) $\frac{14}{18}$ (   )

17. Express 8.45 as a fraction in its simplest form.

    (1) $8\frac{9}{20}$ (2) $8\frac{5}{20}$ (3) $8\frac{5}{9}$ (4) $8\frac{9}{10}$ (   )

18. $\frac{5}{9}$ of the students in a class are girls. There are 25 girls.
    How many boys are there in the class?
    (1) 15   (2) 17   (3) 19   (4) 20   (   )

19. The difference between $\frac{1}{10}$ and $\frac{3}{5}$ is _____ .

    (1) $\frac{7}{10}$ (2) $\frac{1}{2}$ (3) $\frac{4}{5}$ (4) $\frac{3}{5}$ (   )

20. A shopkeeper bought 8 cases of milk. He sold 104 cartons
    of milk and had 88 cartons left. How many cartons of milk
    were there in each case?
    (1) 32   (2) 28
    (3) 24   (4) 18   (   )

B. Write your answers in the boxes provided. (40 points)

21. The sum of 2.9 and 4.56 when rounded off to 1 decimal place is _____.

22. The difference between 7.5 and 6.93 is _____.

23. In 85.06, the digit 6 is in the _____ place.

24. 35.25, 34.95, [_____],34.35.
The missing number is _____.

25. Express $8\frac{3}{5}$ as a decimal.

26. Write the value of $16 + \frac{2}{10} + \frac{7}{100} + \frac{3}{1000}$ as a decimal.

27. In $93.5 +$ [_____] $= 93.59$, the missing decimal is _____.

28. In [_____] $+ 0.65 = 1$, the missing decimal is _____.

29. Express 120 cm as a fraction of 2 m. (Give your answer in its simplest form.)

30.

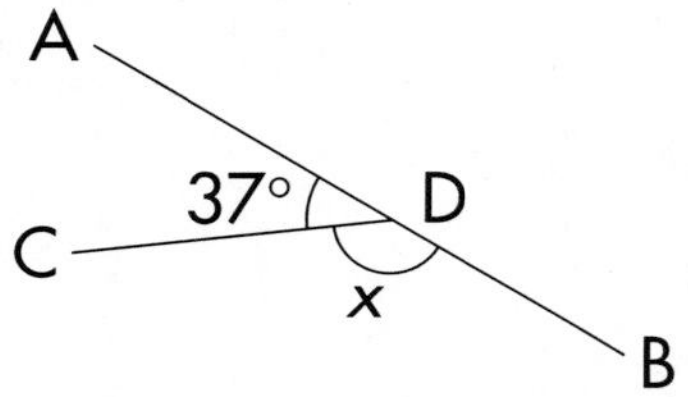

A

37°   D

C

x

B

In the figure, $\angle x$ is _____°.

100

31. 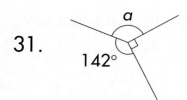 In the figure, $\angle a = $ _____ °.

32. A scientist discovered that a wild elephant needs 200 kg of food every day while a tame elephant needs only 85 kg. How much more food will the wild elephant need in 58 days?

33. Find $\angle x$ in the rectangle.

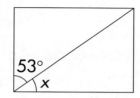

34. Write 8 ones 9 thousandths as a decimal.

35. There are 2153 students in a school. There are 49 more girls than boys. How many boys are there?

36. Chloe bought 45 balloons. $\frac{7}{9}$ of them were yellow. The rest were red. How many red balloons did she buy?

37. Mr. Lewis bought a refrigerator. He paid a down payment of $250 and 12 monthly installments of $85 each. How much did he pay altogether?

38. Mrs. Kim bought an album, a T-shirt and a purse. She paid $26.20 altogether. If the purse cost $12.95 and the T-shirt cost $6.75, what was the cost of the album?

39. There were 24 fine days and 6 rainy days in June last year. What fraction of the month were the rainy days? (Give your answer in its simplest form.) [   ]

40. Mr. Tang spent $\frac{1}{8}$ of his monthly salary on transport.

    He spent 3 times as much money on food as on transport. If his monthly salary was $1760, how much did he spend on food and transport? [   ]

C. Do these problems. Show all your work clearly. (20 points)

41. Tom is 1.68 m tall. He is 0.07 m shorter than his father. If Tom's sister is 1.8 m tall, what is the difference in height between the father and the daughter?

42. A dictionary and a calculator cost $97. If the calculator cost $29 more than the dictionary, what was the cost of the calculator?

43. The area of a rectangle is 104 cm². If its width is 8 cm, find the perimeter of the rectangle.

44. ABCD is a square and CDEF is a rectangle. The perimeter of the square is 20 m. The area of the rectangle is 60 m². What is the perimeter of the rectangle ABFE?

A   D   E

Area = 60 m²

B   C   F

45. $\frac{1}{3}$ of the teachers in a school are male. If there are 48 female teachers in the school, how many teachers are there altogether?

Multiplying Decimals

A. Find the products.

1. $0.5 \times 8 =$

2. $0.9 \times 4 =$

3. $7 \times 0.9 =$

4. $6 \times 0.7 =$

5. $0.04 \times 9 =$

6. $0.07 \times 6 =$

7. $7 \times 0.03 =$

8. $9 \times 0.07 =$

B. Find the products. Show your work.

9. $6.7 \times 3 =$	10. $9 \times 20.6 =$
11. $25.75 \times 4 =$	12. $9 \times 56.08 =$

C. Do these problems. Show all your work clearly.

13. Joe bought 3 story books. Each book cost $4.65. How much did he pay altogether?

14. Adam saved $0.85 each day for 6 days. If he gave his sister $1.25, how much money did he have left?

15. Mrs. Hong bought 3 bath towels at $8.75 each. If she gave the cashier $40, how much change did she receive?

A. Find the quotients in decimals.

1. $0.85 \div 5 =$	2. $0.72 \div 6 =$
3. $0.96 \div 8 =$	4. $0.9 \div 5 =$
5. $0.7 \div 2 =$	6. $8.4 \div 3 =$
7. $16.8 \div 8 =$	8. $48.8 \div 4 =$
9. $40.5 \div 9 =$	10. $60.2 \div 7 =$

B. Find the quotients. Show your work clearly.

11. 7.56 ÷ 3 =	12. 8.45 ÷ 5 =
13. 39.41 ÷ 7 =	14. 68.22 ÷ 9 =

C. Divide. Give your answers in decimals. Show your work clearly.

15. 3 ÷ 4 =	16. 7.3 ÷ 5 =
17. 50.8 ÷ 8 =	18. 51 ÷ 6 =

D. Divide. Give each answer correct to 1 decimal place. Show your work clearly.

19. $15.6 \div 5 =$	20. $23.04 \div 4 =$
21. $20.82 \div 3 =$	22. $41.04 \div 6 =$
23. $64.56 \div 8 =$	24. $21.9 \div 8 =$
25. $38.3 \div 9 =$	26. $123 \div 4 =$

Money: Multiplication and Division (1)

A. Write the amount of money in each set.

1.

(10¢) (25¢)   (10¢) (25¢)

(50¢) (5¢)   (50¢) (5¢)

$$\$0.90 \times 2 = \$ \underline{\hspace{2cm}}$$

2.

(25¢) (10¢) (25¢) (10¢) (25¢) (10¢) (25¢) (10¢)

$$\$0.35 \times 4 = \$ \underline{\hspace{2cm}}$$

3.

| $1 | $1 | | $1 | $1 |

| $1 | (25¢) | | $1 | (25¢) |

$$\$3.25 \times 2 = \$ \underline{\hspace{2cm}}$$

4.

| $5 | | $5 | | $5 |

(50¢) (25¢) (5¢) (50¢) (25¢) (5¢) (50¢) (25¢) (5¢)

$$\$5.80 \times 3 = \$ \underline{\hspace{2cm}}$$

B. Multiply.

5.
$$\begin{array}{r} \$0.55 \\ \times \quad 3 \\ \hline \end{array}$$

6.
$$\begin{array}{r} \$2.25 \\ \times \quad 4 \\ \hline \end{array}$$

7.
$$\begin{array}{r} \$3.70 \\ \times \quad 7 \\ \hline \end{array}$$

8.
$$\begin{array}{r} \$4.05 \\ \times \quad 9 \\ \hline \end{array}$$

9.
$$\begin{array}{r} \$7.65 \\ \times \quad 8 \\ \hline \end{array}$$

10.
$$\begin{array}{r} \$9.20 \\ \times \quad 10 \\ \hline \end{array}$$

C. Divide.

11.
$$2\overline{)\,\$0.70}$$

12.
$$3\overline{)\,\$7.05}$$

13.
$$4\overline{)\,\$4.24}$$

14.
$$6\overline{)\,\$2.70}$$

15.
$$5\overline{)\,\$8.20}$$

16.
$$7\overline{)\,\$5.95}$$

Money: Multiplication and Division (2)

A. Find the total cost.

1.
   $1.45

   1 pen costs $1.45.
   5 pens cost $ _____ .

2. Pigeon
   $5.20

   1 book costs $5.20.
   4 books cost $ _____ .

3. $13.75

   1 bag costs $13.75.
   2 bags cost $ _____ .

B. Complete the bill.

$1.70 $0.50 $136.40 $60.80

4.
1 pair of glasses	$ _____
2 pairs of scissors	$ _____
3 exercise books	$ _____
1 camera	$ _____
Total	$ _____

C. Find the amount.

5. 3 rulers cost $1.35.
1 ruler costs $ _____ .

6. 6 staplers cost $13.20.
1 stapler costs $ _____ .

7. 7 mugs cost $14.35.
1 mug costs $ _____ .

D. Complete the bill.

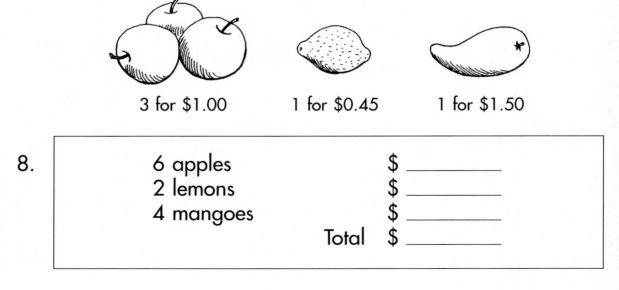

3 for $1.00   1 for $0.45   1 for $1.50

8.

6 apples	$	_____
2 lemons	$	_____
4 mangoes	$	_____
Total	$	_____

Do these problems. Show all your work clearly.

1. Kimberly shared $1.80 equally among her 4 nephews.
    How much money did each nephew get?

2. Melissa bought 5 sets of stamps.
    Each set of stamps costs $1.70.
    How much did she pay altogether?

3. Kate saved $15.35.
    John saved 4 times as much as Kate.
    How much did John save?

4. Mary spent $0.80 in one day.
    How much did she spend in 7 days?

5. Zhenni saved $2.50 in 10 days.
    If she saved an equal amount of money each day, how
    much did she save in one day?

6. David bought 5 tickets which cost $22.50 altogether.
    How much would it cost him to buy 10 tickets?

7. Mrs. King had 5 purses.
   Each purse contained $10.35.
   If she divided the money equally between her 3 daughters,
   how much money did each daughter get?

8. To prepare a gift, Jackie spent $3.15 on a diary and $0.80
   on a wrapping-paper. If she wanted to prepare
   7 such gifts, how much would it cost her?

Do these problems. Show all your work clearly.

1. Catherine cut a ribbon 3.12 yd into 4 equal pieces. She used 3 pieces to tie some packages. How many yards of ribbon did she use?

2. Mrs. Li bought 5 lb of rice. Each pound of rice cost $1.38. She gave the cashier $7. How much change did she receive?

3. A mattress cost $26.50 at a sale. This price was $\frac{2}{3}$ of the usual price. What was the usual price of the mattress?

4. Mrs. Gray weighs 53.7 kg. She is 3 times as heavy as her son. If her husband is 4 times as heavy as her son, what is Mr. Gray's weight?

5. Larry mixed 1.75 ℓ of orange juice with 4 times as much water. He then poured the drink equally into 5 containers. How much drink was there in each container?

6. Karen paid $50.10 for 6 m of cloth and 2 pillows. Each pillow cost $7.50. What was the cost of 1 m of cloth?

Triangles and 4-Sided Figures

A. Name the following triangles.

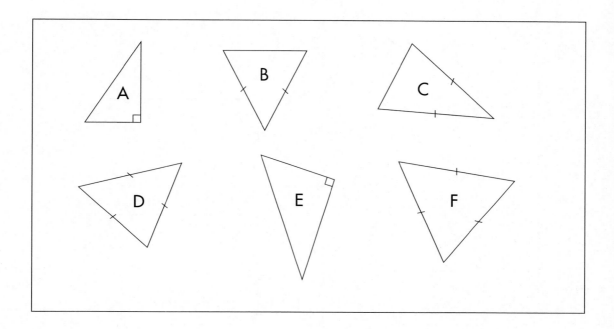

1. Triangle A is a/an _____ triangle.

2. Triangle B is a/an _____ triangle.

3. Triangle C is a/an _____ triangle.

4. Triangle D is a/an _____ triangle.

5. Triangle E is a/an _____ triangle.

6. Triangle F is a/an _____ triangle.

B. Name the following figures.

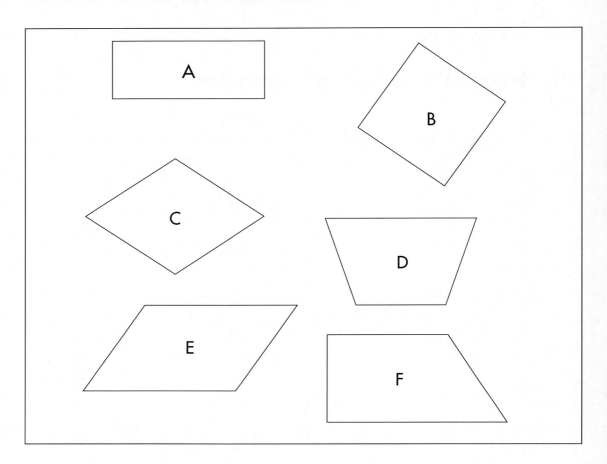

7. Figure A is a _____.

8. Figure B is a _____.

9. Figure C is a _____.

10. Figure D is a _____.

11. Figure E is a _____.

12. Figure F is a _____.

A. **Some of the following figures are symmetric figures. Draw a line of symmetry in each symmetric figure.**

1.

2.

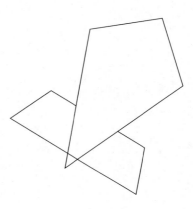

3.

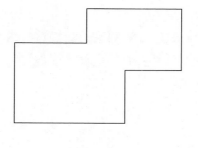

4.

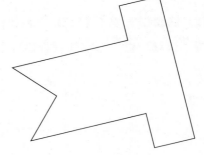

5.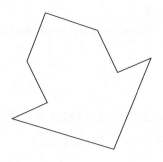

6.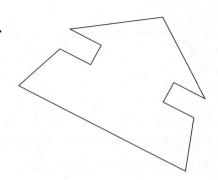

7.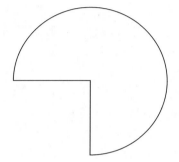

8.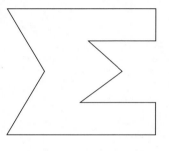

B. **In each of the following figures, is the dotted line a line of symmetry? Answer "Yes" or "No".**

9.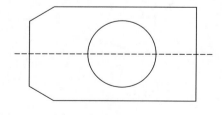

10.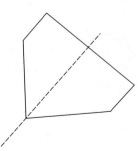

11.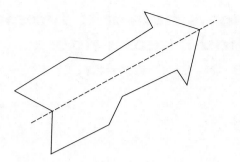

12.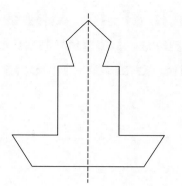

13.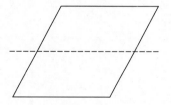

14.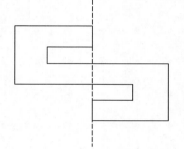

15.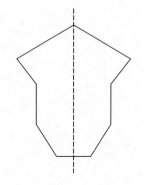

16.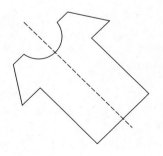

C. Each of the following shows half of a symmetric figure. Draw the other half of each figure. (The dotted line is a line of symmetry.)

17.

18.

19.

20.

21.

22.

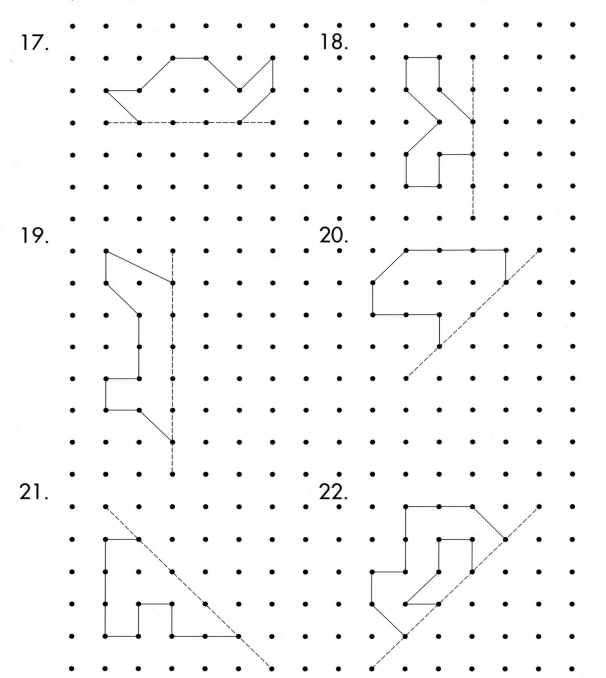

124

A. Find the volume of each solid.

1.

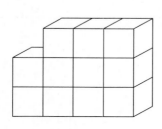

_____ cubic units

2.

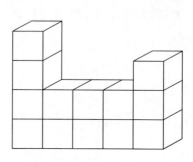

_____ cubic units

3.

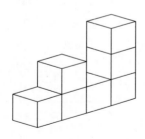

_____ cubic units

4.

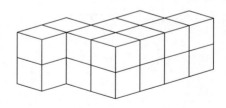

_____ cubic units

5.

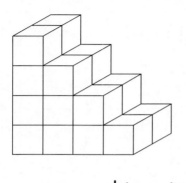

_____ cubic units

6.

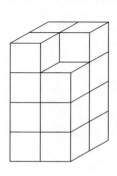

_____ cubic units

7. Which solid has the greatest volume? _____

8. Which solid has the smallest volume? _____

B. **The following solids are made up of 1-cm cubes. Find the volume of each solid.**

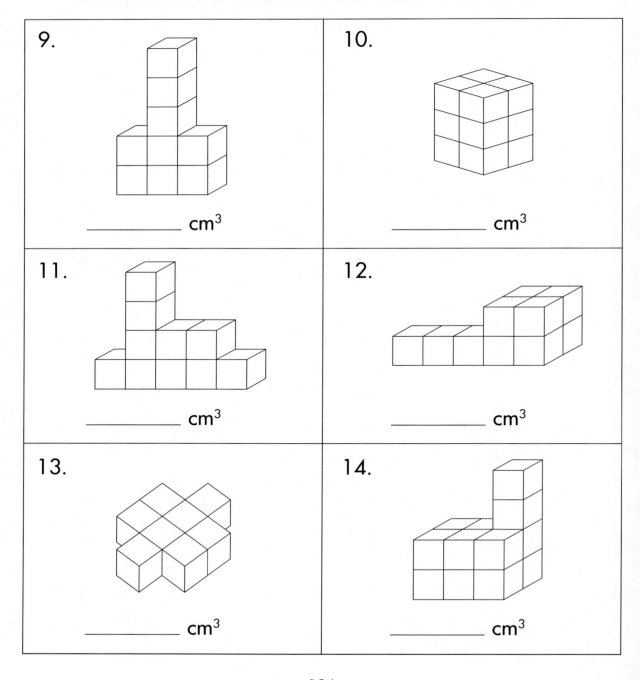

9.

_____ cm³

10.

_____ cm³

11.

_____ cm³

12.

_____ cm³

13.

_____ cm³

14.

_____ cm³

C. The solids are made up of 1-cm cubes. Complete the table below the solids.

15.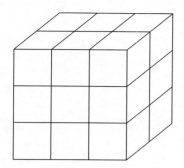

16.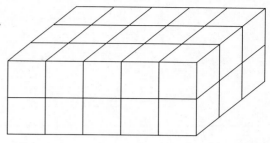

17.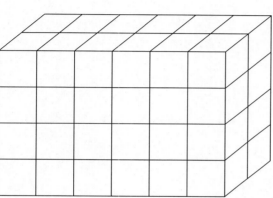

18.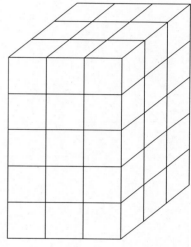

19.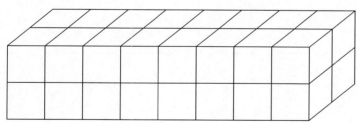

Solid	Length	Width	Height	Volume
15.				
16.				
17.				
18.				
19.				

D. Find the volume of each cuboid. Show your work.

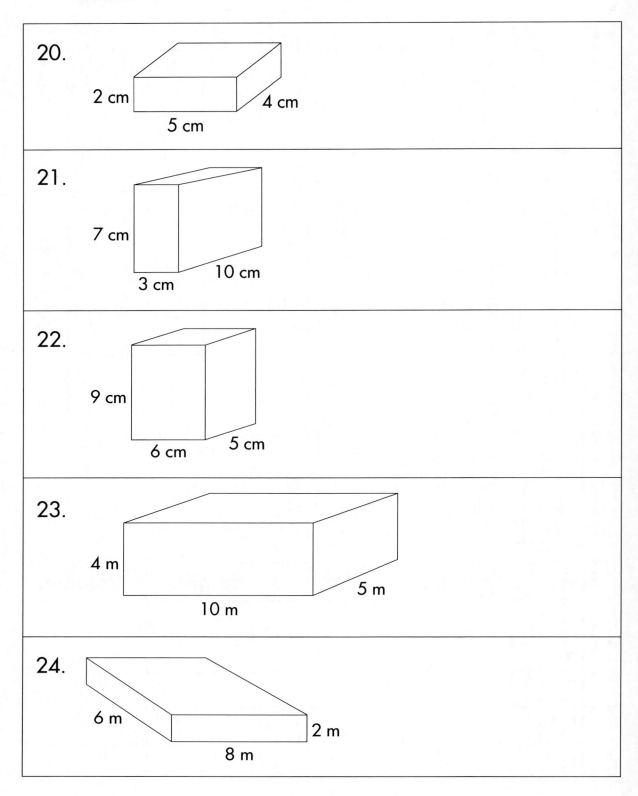

20.

2 cm   4 cm   5 cm

21.

7 cm   3 cm   10 cm

22.

9 cm   6 cm   5 cm

23.

4 m   10 m   5 m

24.

6 m   8 m   2 m

E. **Write the volume of the water in cubic centimeters. (1 ℓ = 1000 cm³)**

25.

_____ cm³

26.

_____ cm³

F. **Write the volume of the water in milliliters. (1 ml = 1 cm³)**

27.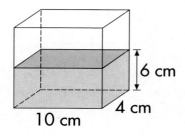

_____ ml

28.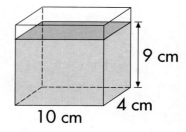

_____ ml

G. **Write the volume of the water in liters. (1 ℓ = 1000 cm³)**

29.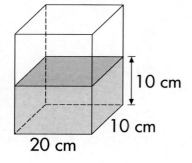

_____ ℓ

30.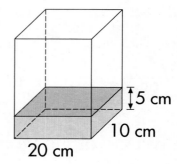

_____ ℓ

H. Find the volume of the water in liters and milliliters.

31.

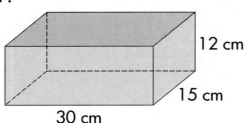

The volume of the water is _____.

32.

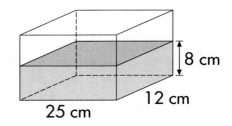

The volume of the water is _____.

33.

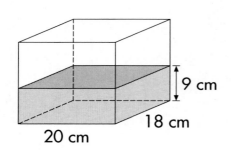

The volume of the water is _____.

34.

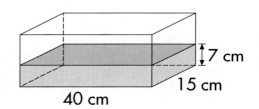

The volume of the water is _____.

35.

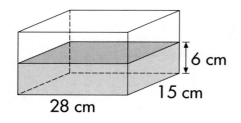

The volume of the water is _____.

36.

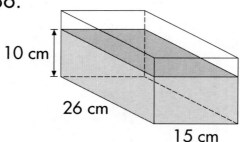

The volume of the water is _____.

A. **Choose the correct answer and write its number in the parentheses provided. (40 points)**

1. There are about 26,800 books in a school library. Which one of the following could be the actual number of books?
    (1) 26,903   (2) 26,859
    (3) 26,835   (4) 26,368   (   )

2. $7 + 7 + 7 + 7 + 7 + \boxed{} = 10 \times 7$.
    The missing number in the box is _____ .
    (1) 25   (2) 27   (3) 35   (4) 37   (   )

3. Which one of the following has 8 as a factor?
    (1) 108   (2) 128   (3) 158   (4) 198   (   )

4. Which one of the following is equal to $\dfrac{3}{4}$?

    (1) $\dfrac{18}{24}$ (2) $\dfrac{12}{18}$ (3) $\dfrac{6}{10}$ (4) $\dfrac{18}{36}$ (   )

5. Write 65 tenths as a decimal.
    (1) 0.65   (2) 5.6   (3) 6.5   (4) 65.0   (   )

6. Which one of the following is the greatest?

    (1) $\dfrac{5}{6}$ (2) $\dfrac{3}{4}$ (3) $\dfrac{7}{8}$ (4) $\dfrac{10}{12}$ (   )

7. In 5.703, the value of the digit 3 is 3 _____ .
    (1) ones   (2) tenths
    (3) hundredths   (4) thousandths   (   )

8. 179.84 when rounded off to 1 decimal place is _____ .
   (1) 179.5   (2) 179.8   (3) 179.9   (4) 180   (   )

9. The volume of the cuboid shown here is _____ .
   (1) 60 cm^3
   (2) 250 cm^3
   (3) 1500 cm^3
   (4) 3000 cm^3 (   )

10. 10 ÷ 8 = _____ .
    (1) 1.5   (2) 1.25   (3) 1.2   (4) 0.8   (   )

11. $6.18 = 6 + \dfrac{1}{10} + \dfrac{8}{\square}$. The missing denominator is _____ .

    (1) 20   (2) 50   (3) 80   (4) 100   (   )

12. $40.3 ÷ 5 = \boxed{} × 2$. The missing number is _____ .
    (1) 4.03   (2) 8.6   (3) 16.12   (4) 17.2   (   )

13. Which one of the following is a symmetric figure?

    (1)   (2)   (3)   (4)   (   )

14. Which of the following is a trapezoid?

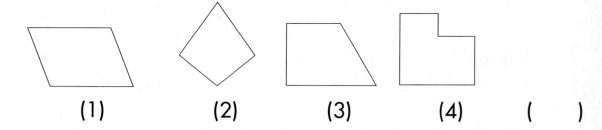

    (1)   (2)   (3)   (4)   (   )

15. Sean bought 3 pens and a file for $6.50. If each pen cost $1.25, how much did the file cost?
    (1) $2.75   (2) $2.95   (3) $3.25   (4) $3.75   (   )

16. The product of 2.25 and 8 is _____ .
    (1) 16.2   (2) 16.4   (3) 18   (4) 20   (   )

17. The perimeter of a square flower bed is 60 m. Find its area.
    (1) 3600 m²   (2) 360 m²
    (3) 240 m²   (4) 225 m²   (   )

18. The area of a rectangular garden is 200 yd². Its width is 8 yd. Find its perimeter.
    (1) 25 yd   (2) 50 yd   (3) 66 yd   (4) 100 yd (   )

19. A tank can hold 18 gallons of water. If it is $\frac{3}{4}$ full, how much more water can be poured in?
    (1) 1 gal 2qt   (2) 4 gal 2qt
    (3) 9 gal   (4) 13 gal 1qt   (   )

20. A shopkeeper sold $\frac{2}{3}$ of his eggs. He had 90 eggs left. How many eggs did he have at first?
    (1) 150   (2) 180   (3) 240   (4) 270   (   )

B. Do the problems and write the answers in the boxes provided. (40 points)

21. The digit 7 in 37,906 stands for 7 × _____ .

22. Write 5 tens 8 hundredths as a decimal.

23. Estimate the sum of 5236, 694 and 3792 by first rounding off each number to the nearest hundred.

24. Which one of the following is the same as 2.2?

$$2\frac{1}{10}, \quad 2\frac{1}{2}, \quad 2\frac{1}{5}, \quad 2\frac{2}{5}$$

25.  $\angle x = $ _____

26. 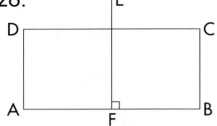 ABCD is a rectangle.
EF ⊥ AB.
EF // ☐ // ☐

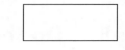

27. Julie had $1.20. She bought a pen for 80 cents. What fraction of the money had she left?

28. Rebecca earned $960 a month. She spent $\frac{5}{8}$ of it and saved the rest. How much money did she save?

29. A ribbon 5.4 m long is cut into 5 equal pieces. How long is each piece?

30. After selling $\frac{2}{5}$ of his melons, Cameron had 27 melons left. How many melons did he sell?

31. The sum of two numbers is 80. If one number is 12 more than the other, find the two numbers.

32. Mark sold 4 cans of milk powder. Three of the smaller cans cost $10.65 each. If he collected $51.75 altogether from the sale, what was the cost of the bigger can of milk powder?

33. The difference between 2.93 and 3.2 is

   _____ .

34. Draw a line of symmetry for the symmetric figure shown here.

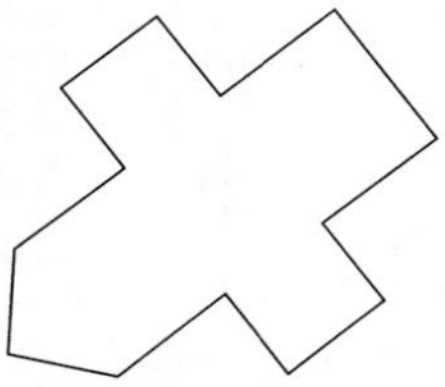

35. Find the difference between the largest 5-digit number and the smallest 4-digit number.

36. In the figure, all the angles are right angles. The area of the shaded part is _____ m^2.

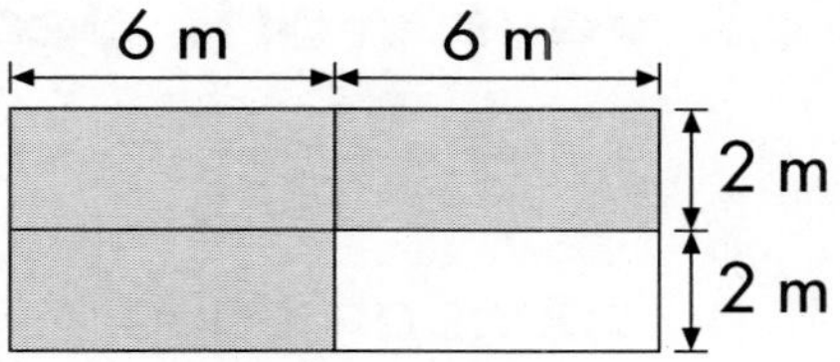

37. James weighs 52.7 kg. He is twice as heavy as his sister. Find their total weight.

38. $\frac{3}{8}$ of a sum of money is $36. Find the whole sum of money.

39. Mrs. Milan made 276 tarts in the morning and 189 tarts in the afternoon. After giving 180 tarts to her friends, she kept the rest equally in 3 containers. How many tarts were there in each container?

40. The graph below shows the weight of fish sold by a market in 5 days. Study the graph and answer the question that follows.

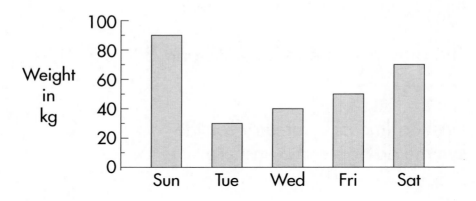

If the market sold the fish at $8 per kg, how much did it earn altogether during the 5 days?

C. Do these problems. Show all your work clearly. (20 points)

41. John spent $4680 in 5 months. If he spent an equal amount each month, how much would he spend in a year?

42. Mrs. Tang bought some sugar. She used $\frac{5}{8}$ of it and had 750 g left. How much sugar did she buy?
(Give your answer in kilograms.)

43. There were some pegs in a basket. $\frac{1}{6}$ of them were red, $\frac{1}{4}$ of them were yellow and the rest were green. If there were 63 green pegs, how many pegs were there altogether?

44. A piece of wire 51 in. long is bent to form a rectangle. If the width of the rectangle is 8 in., find the area formed by the rectangle.

45. A painter mixed 8.5 liters of blue paint and 17.5 liters of yellow paint. After using 9.5 liters of the mixture, he poured the rest equally into 3 tins. How much paint was there in each tin?

Answers

EXERCISE 1

1. 16,080
2. 27,005
3. 80,042
4. 95,600
5. $7305
6. $15,912
7. $90,013
8. $11,460
9. thirty thousand, one hundred eighty dollars
10. nineteen thousand, eleven dollars
11. eighty thousand, eight hundred eighteen
12. twenty-five thousand, three hundred seventy
13. 7200, 7400
14. 33,056, 43,056
15. 20,600, 25,600
16. 10,362, 10,962
17. 5000
18. 30,020
19. 22,066
20. 20,218
21. 3000
22. 6, 10,000
23. hundreds
24. 3, 6
25. 49,326
26. 600
27. 71,900
28. 570
29. $3000
30. 6385, 6538, 30,568, 36,058
31. 39,278, 40,105, 41,062, 51,002
32. 30,000
33. 96,000
34. 18,000
35. 15,000

EXERCISE 2

1. 4023
2. 7776
3. 9064
4. 11,226
5. 13,000
6. 10,295
7. 2668
8. 2101
9. 2373
10. 17
11. 6012
12. 937
13. $266
14. 220

EXERCISE 3

1. 7
2. 18
3. 25
4. 8
5. 1, 2, 3, 6, 9, 18
6. 1, 3, 9, 27, 81
7. 1, 2, 4, 7, 8, 14, 28, 56
8. 1, 2, 7, 14, 49, 98
9. 4
10. 3
11. 12
12. 9
13. Yes
14. 1, 2, 3, 6
15. 3, 6, 9, 12
16. 5, 10, 15, 20
17. 7, 14, 21, 28
18. 9, 18, 27, 36
19. 18, 36
20. 12, 24

EXERCISE 4

1. 536
2. 801
3. 4230
4. 4172
5. 55,032
6. 20,272
7. 28
8. 56
9. 168
10. 906
11. 738
12. 563
13. 5040
14. 51,120
15. 1932
16. 40,000
17. 62,426
18. 23,414
19. 571 R5
20. 652 R3

EXERCISE 5

1. $650
2. 5940
3. 536 g
4. 804
5. 100
6. $500

EXERCISE 6

1. 2
2. 4
3. 15
4. 9
5. 10
6. 28
7. 9
8. 6
9. 12
10. 5
11. 5
12. 7
13. 3, 12, 9
14. 15, 15, 40
15. $\frac{3}{4}$
16. $\frac{1}{4}$
17. $\frac{2}{3}$
18. $\frac{2}{3}$
19. $\frac{1}{2}$
20. $\frac{2}{3}$
21. $\frac{10}{20}$, $\frac{7}{10}$, $\frac{4}{5}$
22. $\frac{2}{3}$, $\frac{9}{12}$, $\frac{5}{6}$
23. $\frac{5}{9}$, $\frac{2}{3}$, $\frac{5}{6}$
24. Dani
25. Melon, papaya

EXERCISE 7

1. $\frac{6}{8}$, $\frac{7}{8}$
2. $\frac{2}{6}$, $\frac{3}{6}$
3. $\frac{2}{5}$
4. $\frac{5}{7}$
5. $\frac{4}{5}$
6. $\frac{2}{3}$
7. $\frac{2}{3}$
8. 1
9. $\frac{1}{2}$
10. $\frac{2}{3}$
11. $\frac{3}{5}$
12. $\frac{3}{4}$
13. $\frac{3}{4}$
14. $\frac{11}{12}$
15. $\frac{3}{4}$
16. $\frac{5}{6}$
17. $\frac{3}{4}$
18. 1
19. 1
20. $\frac{5}{6}$

EXERCISE 8

1. $\frac{2}{4}$
2. $\frac{1}{8}$
3. $\frac{4}{6}$, $\frac{3}{6}$
4. $\frac{6}{8}$, $\frac{1}{8}$
5. $\frac{1}{2}$
6. $\frac{2}{5}$
7. $\frac{3}{7}$
8. $\frac{1}{3}$
9. $\frac{1}{5}$
10. $\frac{1}{6}$
11. $\frac{1}{6}$
12. $\frac{1}{2}$
13. $\frac{5}{9}$
14. $\frac{1}{2}$
15. $\frac{1}{4}$
16. $\frac{4}{5}$
17. $\frac{1}{4}$
18. $\frac{1}{5}$
19. 0
20. $\frac{1}{3}$
21. $\frac{1}{5}$
22. $\frac{1}{2}$

EXERCISE 9

1. $\frac{3}{7}$
2. $\frac{5}{8}$ ft
3. Andrew, $\frac{1}{4}$
4. $\frac{3}{4}$
5. $\frac{7}{10}$ kg

EXERCISE 10

1. $2\frac{1}{2}$ 2. $3\frac{2}{3}$ 3. $2\frac{3}{4}$ 4. $7\frac{5}{8}$ 5. $2\frac{7}{8}$ 6. $3\frac{3}{4}$

7. $1\frac{1}{3}$ 8. $4\frac{3}{5}$ 9. $\frac{10}{5}$ 10. $\frac{9}{4}$ 11. $\frac{18}{6}$ 12. $\frac{11}{3}$

13. 12   14. 10   15. 7   16. 7   17. 5   18. 11

19. $1\frac{4}{5}$ 20. 3   21 $3\frac{3}{4}$ 22. $1\frac{9}{10}$ 23. $1\frac{2}{3}$ 24. $2\frac{5}{6}$

25. $6\frac{1}{2}$ 26. 9   27. $2\frac{1}{2}$ 28. $1\frac{1}{5}$ 29. $7\frac{1}{2}$ 30. $4\frac{1}{3}$

31. $1\frac{5}{7}$ 32. $2\frac{2}{5}$ 33. $\frac{11}{6}$ 34. $\frac{25}{9}$ 35. $\frac{39}{10}$ 36. $\frac{55}{12}$

CONTINUAL ASSESSMENT 1

1. (3)   2. (3)   3. (2)   4. (3)   5. (2)

6. (3)   7. (3)   8. (1)   9. (3)   10. (1)

11. (3)   12. (2)   13. (1)   14. (3)   15. (3)

16. (4)   17. (1)   18. (2)   19. (4)   20. (3)

21. 40,015   22. 9732   23. 400   24. 89,900   25. 1000

26. hundreds   27. $79,000   28. 5, 10   29. 5   30. 36

31. $\frac{41}{12}$ 32. $2\frac{1}{3}$ 33. $\frac{1}{2}$, $\frac{5}{8}$, $\frac{3}{4}$ 34. 7   35. $1\frac{1}{3}$

36. $\frac{1}{4}$ or $\frac{3}{12}$ 37. $3\frac{3}{5}$ 38. $\frac{1}{8}$ lb   39. $\frac{3}{8}$ 40. 31

41. $2268   42. $622   43. $30   44. $21   45. 36

EXERCISE 11

1. $4\frac{1}{2}$ 2. 8   3. 4   4. 6   5. 8   6. $10\frac{1}{2}$

7. $3\frac{1}{3}$ 8. 15   9. $2\frac{2}{3}$ 10. $4\frac{1}{2}$ 11. $7\frac{1}{2}$ 12. 6

13. $8\frac{1}{3}$ 14. $1\frac{1}{2}$ 15. $4\frac{2}{3}$ 16. $5\frac{2}{5}$ 17. 6   18. EAT WISELY

EXERCISE 12

1. 8   2. 6   3. 20   4. 10   5. 24   6. 35

7. 96   8. 112   9. $7\frac{1}{2}$ 10. $3\frac{1}{3}$ 11. $5\frac{3}{5}$ 12. $7\frac{1}{2}$

13. $16\frac{2}{3}$ 14. $11\frac{2}{3}$ 15. $12\frac{1}{2}$ 16. $4\frac{1}{2}$

EXERCISE 13

1. $\frac{2}{5}$ 2. $\frac{3}{5}$ 3. $\frac{3}{4}$ 4. $\frac{7}{20}$ 5. $\frac{2}{3}$ 6. $\frac{1}{4}$

7. $\frac{1}{3}$ 8. $\frac{3}{5}$ 9. $\frac{1}{5}$ 10. $\frac{1}{4}$

EXERCISE 14

1. 9 kg   2. 28   3. 16   4. $40, $60   5. 21   6. 40, 16

7. $80, $24   8. 19   9. $450

EXERCISE 15

1. 51   2. 12   3. 12   4. $120

5. 17; 13, 49; 53, 85   6. 21   7. 13   8. 73

9. 1550   10. 2300   11. 250   12. $5330

13. 75 ml, $1.55; 125 ml, $2.20; 200 ml, $3.50   14. $11.65

15. $4.05   16. $0.25

EXERCISE 16

1. 5   2. 7   3. 6   4. 4

5. 3   6. 2   7. 4   8. 5

9. school   10. tree   11. hill   12. school

13. bus stop   14. tree   15. school

EXERCISE 17

1. ∠a, ∠b, ∠c, ∠d, ∠h, ∠k, ∠q, ∠y, ∠z   2. ∠e, ∠f, ∠n, ∠o, ∠p, ∠r, ∠u, ∠v, ∠x

3. ∠g, ∠i, ∠j, ∠l, ∠m, ∠s, ∠t, ∠w   4. 45°   5. 90°

6. 120°   7. 105°   8. 67°   9. 155°

10. 75°   11. 38°   12. 110°   13. 165°

14. 123°   15. 136°

EXERCISE 18

1. 50°   2. 25°   3. 34°   4. 55°   5. 38°   6. 108°

EXERCISE 19

1. 4, 360
2. 2, 180
3. 1, 90
4. 3, 270
5. 220°
6. 310°
7. 245°
8. 335°
9. 151°
10. 46°
11. 35°
12. 324°
13. 217°
14. 58°

EXERCISE 20

1. EA ⊥ AB; CD ⊥ ED
2. FE ⊥ IE; FG ⊥ HG; HI ⊥ EI
3. JK ⊥ JO; ON ⊥ MN
4. PT ⊥ ST; TS ⊥ RS; PQ ⊥ RQ

5.
6.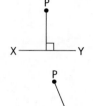
7.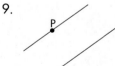
8.

9.
10.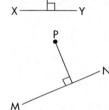

EXERCISE 21

1. CD // GH
2. MP // NO
3. WZ // XY; WX // ZY
4. SR // PQ; PT // QR
5.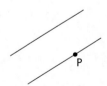
6.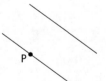

7.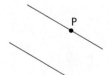
8.
9.
10.

11. 4 cm, 11 cm
12. 7 cm, 10 cm
13. 5 cm, 15 cm, 12 cm

EXERCISE 22

1. 18 cm², 18 cm
2. 20 cm², 18 cm
3. 36 m², 24 m
4. 108 cm²
5. $480
6. $792
7. 64 cm²
8. 20 in.
9. 3 ft, square
10. 5 m, 22 m
11. (a) 6 cm, 54 cm²
(b) 12 m, 60 m²
12. (A) 4 m, 26 m
(B) 8 yd, 30 yd
(C) 16 m, 48 m
(D) 13 ft, 44 ft
(E) 15 cm, 50 cm

EXERCISE 23

1. 134 m   2. 90 m   3. 72 cm   4. 332 cm²   5. 334 cm²   6. 570 m²
7. 160 m²   8. 284 cm²   9. 204 m²   10. 90 ft²   11. 18 yd²

SEMESTER ASSESSMENT 1

1. (3)   2. (3)   3. (2)   4. (3)   5. (2)   6. (4)
7. (3)   8. (2)   9. (4)   10. (3)   11. (3)   12. (2)
13. (2)   14. (3)   15. (1)   16. (1)   17. (1)   18. (4)
19. (3)   20. (3)   21. 50   22. 4
23. $\frac{2}{3}$ 24. $\frac{7}{12}$, $\frac{5}{6}$, $\frac{12}{8}$, 2   25. 9   26. $79
27. $\frac{5}{12}$ 28. $\frac{1}{6}$ 29. $364   30. 385
31. $60   32. $\frac{3}{4}$ or $\frac{9}{12}$ 33. $\frac{1}{3}$ 34. 304°
35. BC ⊥ DC   36. 45 cm²   37. 1312 m   38. 66 m²
39. $1350   40. $1550   41. $28   42. 30
43. $\frac{3}{10}$ lb   44. $462   45. 116 cm, 486 cm²

EXERCISE 24

1. 0.3   2. 0.8   3. 3.5   4. 1.6   5. 2.7   6. 4.9
7. $\frac{3}{5}$ 8. $\frac{1}{2}$ 9. $\frac{1}{5}$ 10. $1\frac{4}{5}$ 11. $3\frac{2}{5}$ 12. $5\frac{3}{10}$
13. 6.5   14. 3.9   15. 52.6   16. 80.8   17. 0.5   18. 0.2
19. 0.4   20. 2, 9, 3

EXERCISE 25

1. 0.05   2. 0.08   3. 0.39   4. 0.63
5. 3.01   6. 7.06   7. 10.99   8. 9.56
9. hundredths, 0.09   10. tenths, 0.6   11. 30.2   12. 16.9
13. 29.03   14. 62.51   15. 0.08   16. 0.07
17. 0.4   18. 0.1, 0.01   19. 9   20. 13
21. 25   22. 5   23. 36   24. 70
25. 100   26. 180   27. 0.9, 1   28. 1.5, 2
29. 0.15, 0.1   30. 3.6, 3.4   31. 1.25, 1   32. $\frac{4}{5}$
33. $7\frac{2}{5}$ 34. $\frac{1}{4}$ 35. $3\frac{3}{4}$ 36. $\frac{3}{50}$

37. $4\frac{1}{50}$

38. $\frac{7}{20}$

39. $8\frac{9}{20}$

40. 0.2

41. 5.5

42. 10.4

43. 0.25

44. 0.75

45. 2.75

46. 0.95

47. 4.48

EXERCISE 26

1. 0.007
2. 0.009
3. 0.023
4. 0.056
5. 0.135
6. 0.792
7. 9.005
8. 30.018
9. thousandths, 0.008
10. thousandths, 0.003
11. 0.002
12. 0.006
13. 0.007
14. 7
15. 39
16. 1000
17. 12.001
18. 8.025
19. 25.403
20. 7.068
21. 0.002
22. 0.038
23. 0.705
24 6.006
25. 90.009

EXERCISE 27

1. 0.95
2. 0.736
3. 6.999
4. 0.86
5. 5
6. 4.01
7. 2.2
8. 6.1
9. 30
10. 59.68
11. 84
12. 62.3
13. 76.99
14. 28.83
15. 20
16. 30.09
17. 0.9
18. 6

EXERCISE 28

1. 6
2. 12
3. 29
4. 61
5. 59
6. 34
7. 8
8. 50
9. 400
10. 205
11. $15
12. $66
13. 37 kg
14. 59 kg
15. 22 yd
16. 92 yd
17. 5 ℓ
18. 17 ℓ
19. 64 km
20. 530 km
21. 69.1
22. 86.5
23. 35.7
24. 164.6
25. 562.0
26. 216.2
27. 35.38 kg

EXERCISE 29

1. 1
2. 1.5
3. 4
4. 6.3
5. 8.7
6. 10.5
7. 36
8. 31.6
9. 49
10. 366.1
11. 286.2
12. 301.4
13. 8.5
14. 4.26
15. 6
16. 23.24
17. 5.25
18. 2.54
19. 24.2
20. 59.14
21. 91.26
22. 46.98
23. 110.65
24. 370.06

EXERCISE 30

1. 0.9	2. 1.8	3. 0.8	4. 3.6	5. 4.5	6. 7.9
7. 0.5	8. 27.2	9. 69.9	10. 4.8	11. 0.23	12. 60.3
13. 2.29	14. 1.36	15. 0.02	16. 8.61	17. 2.99	18. 11.98
19. 0.21	20. 8.75	21. 0.09	22. 4.68	23. 3.07	24. 17.94

EXERCISE 31

1. $9.55	2. 0.05 m	3. 57.15 kg	4. $35.50
5. 76.65 km	6. 11.3 m		

CONTINUAL ASSESSMENT 2

1. (3)	2. (4)	3. (3)	4. (3)	5. (1)
6. (1)	7. (4)	8. (3)	9. (2)	10. (3)
11. (3)	12. (2)	13. (4)	14. (3)	15. (3)
16. (3)	17. (1)	18. (4)	19. (2)	20. (3)
21. 7.5	22. 0.57	23. hundredths	24. 34.65	25. 8.6
26. 16.273	27. 0.09	28. 0.35	29. $\frac{3}{5}$	30. 143°
31. 128°	32. 6670 kg	33. 37°	34. 8.009	35. 1052
36. 10	37. $1270	38. $6.50	39. $\frac{1}{5}$	40. $880
41. 0.05 m	42. $63	43. 42 cm	44. 44 m	45. 72

EXERCISE 32

1. 4	2. 3.6	3. 6.3	4. 4.2	5. 0.36
6. 0.42	7. 0.21	8. 0.63	9. 20.1	10. 185.4
11. 103	12. 504.72	13. $13.95	14. $3.85	15. $13.75

EXERCISE 33

1. 0.17	2. 0.12	3. 0.12	4. 0.18	5. 0.35
6. 2.8	7. 2.1	8. 12.2	9. 4.5	10. 8.6
11. 2.52	12. 1.69	13. 5.63	14. 7.58	15. 0.75
16. 1.46	17. 6.35	18. 8.5	19. 3.1	20. 5.8
21. 6.9	22. 6.8	23. 8.1	24. 2.7	25. 4.3
26. 30.8				

EXERCISE 34

1. 1.80	2. 1.40	3. 6.50	4. 17.40
5. $1.65	6. $9.00	7. $25.90	8. $36.45
9. $61.20	10. $92.00	11. $0.35	12. $2.35
13. $1.06	14. $0.45	15. $1.64	16. $0.85

EXERCISE 35

1. 7.25	2. 20.80	3. 27.50	4. 60.80, 3.40, 1.50, 136.40, 202.10
5. 0.45	6. 2.20	7. 2.05	8. $2.00, $0.90, $6.00, $8.90

EXERCISE 36

1. $0.45	2. $8.50	3. $61.40	4. $5.60	5. $0.25
6. $45	7. $17.25	8. $27.65		

EXERCISE 37

1. 2.34 m	2. 10¢	3. $39.75	4. 71.6 kg
5. 1.75 ℓ	6. $5.85		

EXERCISE 38

1. right-angled	2. isosceles	3. isosceles
4. equilateral	5. right-angled	6. equilateral
7. rectangle	8. square	9. rhombus
10. trapezoid	11. parallelogram	12. trapezoid

EXERCISE 39

1. 　　2. 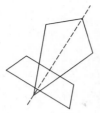　　3. 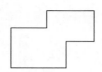　　4.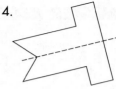

5. 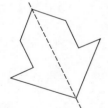　　6. 　　7. 　　8.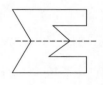

9. Yes	10. Yes	11. Yes	12. Yes
13. No	14. No	15. Yes	16. Yes

17.   18.   19. 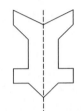   20.

21.   22.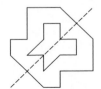

EXERCISE 40

1. 11	2. 13	3. 7	4. 18	5. 20
6. 15	7. No. 5	8. No. 3	9. 9	10. 12
11. 10	12. 11	13. 8	14. 14	

Solid	Length	Width	Height	Volume
15.	3	2	3	18 cm^3
16.	5	3	2	30 cm^3
17.	6	2	4	48 cm^3
18.	3	3	5	45 cm^3
19.	8	2	2	32 cm^3

20. 40 cm^3 21. 210 cm^3 22. 270 cm^3 23. 200 m^3 24. 96 m^3
25. 700   26. 200   27. 240   28. 360   29. 2
30. 1   31. 5 ℓ 400 ml   32. 2 ℓ 400 ml   33. 3 ℓ 240 ml   34. 4 ℓ 200 ml
35. 2 ℓ 520 ml   36. 3 ℓ 900 ml

SEMESTER ASSESSMENT 2

1. (3)   2. (3)   3. (2)   4. (1)   5. (3)   6. (3)
7. (4)   8. (2)   9. (3)   10. (2)   11. (4)   12. (1)
13. (2)   14. (3)   15. (1)   16. (3)   17. (4)   18. (3)
19. (2)   20. (4)   21. 1000   22. 50.08   23. 9700   24. $2\frac{1}{5}$
25. 312°   26. DA, CB   27. $\frac{1}{3}$ 28. $360   29. 1.08 m   30. 18
31. 34, 46   32. $19.80   33. 0.27   34.   35. 98,999   36. 36

37. 79.05 kg   38. $96   39. 95   40. $2240   41. $11,232   42. 2 kg
43. 108   44. 140 in.^{2} 45. 5.5 ℓ